CRYOGENICS

RESEARCH and APPLICATIONS

CRYOGENICS
RESEARCH and APPLICATIONS

by Marshall Sittig

ASSISTANT DIRECTOR
in the office of Research Administration
Princeton University, Princeton, New Jersey

Illustrated by Stephen Kidd

ASSISTANT DIRECTOR
in the Office of Research Administration
Princeton University, Princeton, New Jersey

D. VAN NOSTRAND COMPANY, INC.
PRINCETON, NEW JERSEY
Toronto New York London

D. VAN NOSTRAND COMPANY, INC.

120 Alexander St., Princeton, New Jersey (*Principal office*)
24 West 40 Street, New York 18, New York

D. VAN NOSTRAND COMPANY, LTD.
358, Kensington High Street, London, W.14, England

D. VAN NOSTRAND COMPANY (Canada), LTD.
25 Hollinger Road, Toronto 16, Canada

Published simultaneously in Canada by
D. VAN NOSTRAND COMPANY (Canada), LTD.

PRINTED IN THE UNITED STATES OF AMERICA

CONTENTS

INTRODUCTION

The world of low temperatures offers immediate promise in such diverse areas as the manufacture of more compact computer memories and the breeding of better cattle by artificial insemination, or in the improved performance of oil wells and the economical transport of ice cream. The phenomena encountered at low temperatures, where electric currents flow continuously in cold metal without an external voltage once they are started, and where fluids climb out of their containers, have been the subject of many learned papers and books by physicists; indeed there has been a tendency to lump together many interesting and useful phenomena under the heading of cryophysics, a formidable heading indeed.

It is the thesis of this book that one need not be a physicist to learn about the interesting possibilities of working at low temperatures and to put these possibilities to work. This book is directed to the biologist, the chemist, the electrical engineer, or just the inquiring reader who finds here a connection with his or her interests and is tempted to explore the cold frontier.

Chapter 1

THE REALLY NEW FRONTIER

As man ventures further into space and delves further into the ultimate structure of matter, he encounters a new frontier — the cold frontier. Figure 1-1 shows the cold frontier in outer space.

Cold is, of course, a relative term. We may say that we are "cold" when we come out of the hot sun into the shade. The coldest spots on the face of the earth dip only to around —90°F (—68°C) during the Arctic winter. Solid carbon dioxide, or "Dry Ice" at —109°F (—78°C) is the coldest substance with which we usually have any contact in our everyday lives.

Just as we have taken great strides in the handling and use of very high temperatures, in such applications as blast furnaces and the re-entry of space vehicles, now we are coming to a new appreciation of the problems and possibilities of operating devices at really low temperatures. As used here, this term does not denote the range cited above, the first hundred degrees below zero Fahrenheit, but rather the range from —148°F (—100°C) down almost to absolute zero —459°F (—273°C).

This is the realm where gases of the air turn liquid, where steel becomes brittle as glass, where metals become superconductive, and where living cells pass into a state of suspended animation.

In Gulliver's account of his travels, he describes work at the mythical Academy of Lagado where "Some (workers) were condensing air into a dry tangible substance by extracting the niter, and letting the aqueous or fluid particles percolate." Thus,

1

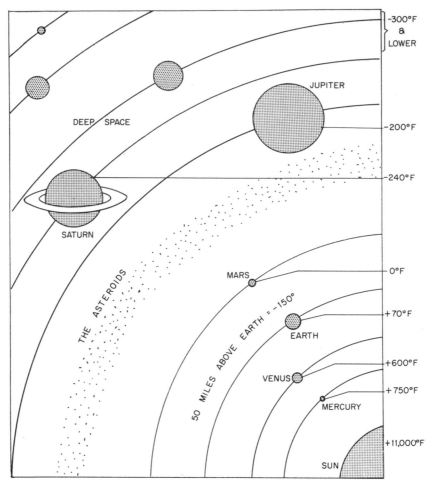

Fig. 1-1 Temperature around the solar system.

in 1726, the author Jonathan Swift predicted the liquefaction of
air, an event which was not to occur for 150 years.

In 1894 Raoul Pictet, who was one of the first to liquefy oxygen,
went on to apply his knowledge of low temperatures to a study
of their effects on the human body. He advocated exposure
in a "cold well" to temperatures of —90 to —110°C (—130 to
—166°F) for periods of 8 to 12 or even 15 minutes and called
such treatments frigotherapy. Pictet himself claimed that he
had suffered from dyspepsia for years but that after 15 minutes

in the cold well, he emerged and ate a full meal with enjoyment for the first time in six years. Regardless of the truth of Pictet's case, he may have forecast the present, when cryosurgery is about to be realized.

WHAT IS CRYOGENICS?

The realm of cryogenics is defined here as the temperature range below —100°C (—148°F), extending down to absolute zero, —273°C (—459°F).

The word cryo-genics means relating to cold, being derived from the Greek words "kryos" which means "icy-cold" and "genes" which means "born." According to authorities at Arthur D. Little, Inc., this word dates from about 1875, but it does not seem to have been used to any great extent before about 1955; prior to that date one finds most authors using the term "low temperature" to describe the really low temperature research and applications of the science of cryogenics, which date back to about 1900 when the cryogenic gases were first produced.

WHAT ARE THE CRYOGENIC GASES?

The cryogenic gases are those gases whose boiling points are below —100°C (—148°F). Thus they include the most common atmospheric gases: nitrogen, oxygen and argon, and also include the rarer atmospheric gases: neon, krypton and xenon. Of other gases, the cryogenic group includes helium, hydrogen, methane, and fluorine, and may be said to include ethylene, which is a border-line case, boiling at —104°C (—155°F). The four which are available in the greatest quantities, and which account for most of the cryogenic research and applications are given major attention here. They are oxygen, nitrogen, helium and hydrogen. These four major cryogenic gases may be divided into two groups, characterized as cold and very cold. The components of air boil at about —190°C (—310°F) which is certainly cold, and then hydrogen and helium carry us down to the very cold range of

—250 to —270°C (—418 to —454°F). The great difference between these two temperature levels is shown by the fact that oxygen and nitrogen at liquid hydrogen or liquid helium temperatures have the appearance and mechanical properties which we associate with ordinary white sand at room temperature. Note, however, that many conventional devices continue to function at very low temperatures. Standard fractional horsepower motors have been run successfully in liquid helium, although bearing modifications have been necessary because of the abrasive action of the solidified air within their casings.

It is uncertain when the idea that gases could be liquefied first occurred to a scientist, but Lavoisier expressed the view that if the earth were cooled to the temperature of outer space, at least part of its atmosphere would liquefy. He did no experimental work to verify this supposition, however, and it remained for later investigators to liquefy the components of the air.

Nitrogen

Nitrogen is the major constituent of air, accounting for 78% by volume and for 75.45% by weight. Liquid nitrogen boils at —196°C (—321°F) and freezes at —210°C (—346°F). It was called azote by Lavoisier, which means "without life." The name nitrogen came later, being derived from the Latin word "nitro" meaning "native soda" and the Greek word "genes," meaning "born."

The volume of nitrogen produced is increasing, in fact its growth is among the greatest of present-day chemical materials. It is obtained, along with oxygen, by separation of air. There are about 4 tons of nitrogen available in the air for every ton of oxygen (see Figure 1-2 for the composition of the earth's atmosphere at various levels). Today about 0.5 tons of nitrogen are recovered per ton of oxygen produced, the rest of the nitrogen being vented to the atmosphere. More air separation plants are being built every day, and a greater proportion of nitrogen to oxygen is being recovered as new uses of nitrogen develop, and old ones expand.

In the United States alone, the production of elementary

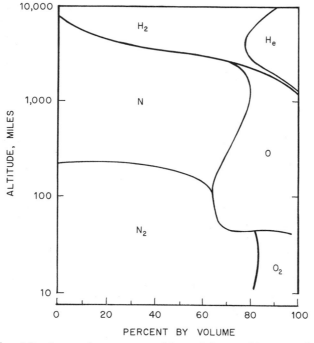

FIG. 1-2 Approximate composition of the earth's atmosphere.

nitrogen in air separation plants today amounts to about 2-3 million tons per year (40-60 billion cubic feet per year). In considering nitrogen production statistics, we must add the "fixed" nitrogen production, which is the source of ammonia, ammomium compounds, nitric acid, nitrates and other important chemicals.)

Major present-day industrial uses of elementary nitrogen are shown in Figure 1-3. They include its uses for:

— Bright annealing of stainless steel — described and illustrated in Chapter 18.
— Flushing, precooling and testing of rockets, and space simulation — described and illustrated in Chapter 11.
— Supplying an inert atmosphere in manufacture of chemicals and metals that react with the oxygen of the air — described in Chapter 17.
— Artificial insemination — to be described and illustrated in Chapter 12.

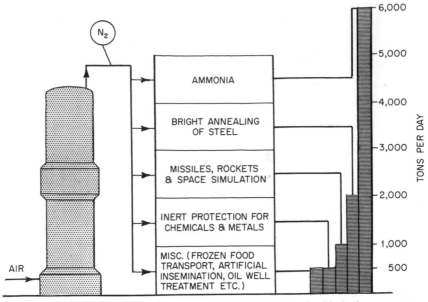

FIG. 1-3   Nitrogen — sources and uses in the U. S. A.

Prospects for large-scale use of nitrogen in coming years include applications in:

— Frozen food transport — described and illustrated in Chapter 13.
— Oil well operations — described and illustrated in Chapter 10.

Oxygen

Oxygen is the second major constituent of air, accounting for 21% of air by volume and for 23.2% by weight. Oxygen liquefies at —183°C (—297°F) and, upon further cooling, solidifies at —218°C (—360°F). It was named oxygen by Lavoisier — the meaning of the word being "I generate life."

The world production of oxygen in 1962 in air separation plants was at the rate of a ton per second. United States capacity is 22,000 tons per day and world capacity is 72,000 tons per day.

Prospects are that United States production will double by 1972 and world production may do likewise.

In its early commercial applications, dating from the beginning of the twentieth century, oxygen was wedded largely to the metals industries. This probably grew from early association of oxygen producers and metals fabricators in the development of oxy-acetylene cutting and welding. Then about 1930 oxygen was first used in steel manufacture in Germany. This type of use has expanded rapidly both in the United States and Europe and perhaps half of all of today's oxygen goes into steel manufacture.

The first commercial use of oxygen to replace air in chemical manufacture also dates from about 1930 and was developed in Germany. This application, unlike the use in steel manufacture, did not really grow until after World War II. Now, however, chemical manufacture has surpassed steel production as a consumer of oxygen, and growth prospects from this point probably exceed those for the steel industry. The U.S. breakdown of oxygen uses today is shown in Figure 1-4.

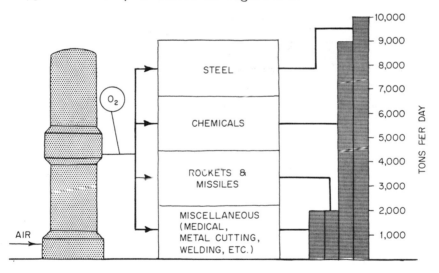

FIG. 1-4 Oxygen — source and uses in the U. S. A.

Since oxygen is now shipped in such enormous volumes, it is being handled much like other chemicals — in tank cars and trucks. Figure 1-5 shows the operation of loading a highway

FIG. 1-5   Loading "Lox" tank trailers.

tank trailer for the transport of liquid oxygen, or "lox" as it is sometimes called.

Argon

The only other constituent of the air which is present to the extent of 1% or more is argon, which constitutes 0.93% by volume and 1.25% of weight of normal dry air. Argon was discovered by Ramsay and Rayleigh in 1894. Its name is derived from the Greek negative prefix "a" and the Greek word "ergon," meaning work, because it did not form chemical compounds (although current research seems likely to find some such compounds) and because it provides no chemical energy. Argon becomes a liquid at —186°C (—303°F) and becomes a solid at —189°C (—308°F). The liquid range is thus seen to be extremely narrow — only 3°C or 5°F; this behavior is also characeristic of neon, which has a narrow liquid range, although the latter is 60°C (108°F) lower than that of argon.

Argon boils between nitrogen and oxygen, slightly closer to oxygen. Thus, producing a crude grade of argon (90 - 95% pure) involves only putting a few extra plates in the air separation column and is fairly easy (See Figure 1-7). This product can then be purified by burning it with hydrogen over a catalyst to remove the oxygen, which is the major impurity. If the nitrogen remaining as an impurity is to be removed, a low temperature distillation is necessary.

Argon is less expensive than helium, and thus has a bright future in shielded-arc welding applications (See Figure 1-6). Other potential uses of argon are in lamps and vacuum tubes. At one time argon appeared to have great promise as a blanketing agent in titanium and zirconium manufacture, in which a cubic foot of argon is needed for every pound of sponge refractory metal produced plus another cubic foot for every pound processed. However, the demand for titanium and zirconium has failed to

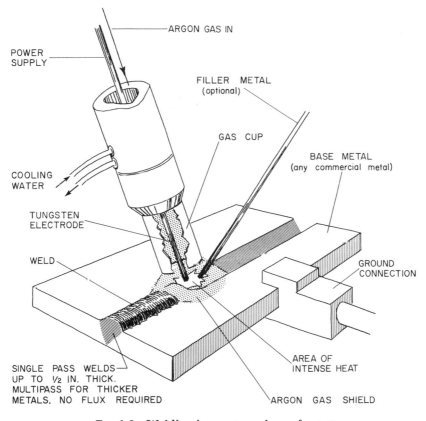

Fig. 1-6 Welding in an atmosphere of argon.

meet the rosy forecasts of several years ago, and the expected argon consumption has dwindled proportionately. A new hope for the use of argon in metallurgy has been offered, however, by furnaces which melt metals at high rates (five times as fast as in an induction furnace) under slag-free, high-purity conditions.

The present argon market is about 570 million cubic feet per year, which is about 100 tons per day. Of this, some 55% goes into nonferrous metals manufacture and welding (See Figure 1-6), some 25% into electronics, and about 10% into the steel industry, with the remaining 10% being used for miscellaneous applications.

Although most commercial argon is produced by air separation (See Figure 1-7), a small quantity of argon is obtained as a by-product of the commercial synthesis of ammonia from nitrogen and hydrogen. In the recycle in an ammonia plant, the argon present in the nitrogen (which was extracted from the air) would tend to build up because of its chemically inert nature. To prevent this accumulation of argon, a portion of the recycle gases must be vented; argon recovery from these vent gases is profitable in some plants.

Neon

Neon was named from the Greek word "neos" which means "new." It was new in 1898 when Ramsay and Travers first isolated it in the fractionation of liquid air. Present to the extent of only about one part in 80,000 in air, neon is truly one of the rare gases, along with its sister elements, krypton and xenon.

Neon becomes a liquid at —246°C (—411°F) and further cooling produces solid neon at —249°C (—416°F).

The chief use of neon is in the electric sign industry. It imparts the characteristic red to orange-red glow and is so closely associated in the popular mind with fluorescent signs that they are all called "neon signs." Other uses of neon, usually in admixture with other gases, are in voltage regulator tubes, Geiger-Müller counter tubes, glow lamps, sodium vapor lamps, and fluorescent tube starter switches.

Liquid neon is becoming of increasing interest as a cryogenic

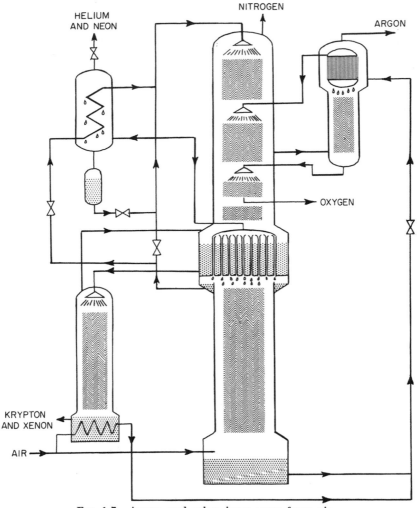

FIG. 1-7   Argon and other inert gases from air.

fluid. Because of its high density and high heat of evaporation, it provides 3½ times more refrigeration than an equal volume of liquid hydrogen, and 40 times more than an equal volume of liquid helium. The inertness of neon is another advantage when it is compared with liquid hydrogen.

Krypton

Krypton was named from the Greek word "kryptos" which means "hidden." It was indeed hidden from the sight of students of the atmosphere, since it is present to the extent of only one part in about 2 million parts of air. It too was discovered by Ramsay and Travers in 1898.

Krypton is about 4 times as heavy as neon, about 3 times as heavy as nitrogen, and about 2.6 times as heavy as oxygen. It condenses to a liquid at —153°C (—243°F) and freezes to a solid at —157°C (—251°F).

Krypton is used mainly in the electronic and lamp industries. Its high atomic weight reduces evaporation and heat losses from filaments, permitting operation of lamps at higher temperatures. In New York City, krypton-filled signal lamps are used in traffic lights because of their long life. Krypton is also used in gaseous encephalography. When blown into the brain ventricles, replacing the liquid normally there, it increases the contrast of X-ray images on film, since krypton is opaque to X-rays. The radioactive isotope of krypton, krypton-85, is finding use in medicine, leak detection, and other applications.

Xenon

Xenon derives its name from the Greek word "xenos," meaning "strange." It is indeed strange among components of air in that it is by far the rarest and heaviest. It is present in air only to the extent of one part in about 170 million parts of air by volume. It is twice as heavy as krypton and about 4 times as heavy as the average of the other constituents of the air.

Xenon liquefies at —163°C (—261°F) and solidifies at —169°C (—272°F). Xenon, like krypton and neon, was first separated from the air in 1898.

The density and inertness of xenon have led to its application in scintillation counters. The electrical properties of xenon are close to those of mercury, and since xenon will not condense readily, it is used to supplement mercury vapor in some thyratron tubes. It has been suggested for use as an anaesthetic, having the virtue of no "hangover" after use.

The recent discovery of xenon tetrafluoride by workers at the Argonne National Laboratory of the U. S. Atomic Energy Commission destroys the concept of the invariable inertness of xenon (and perhaps the other rare gases). This fact once again demonstrates that there are the frontiers of science which are still available for exploration, and re-emphasizes the fact that categorical statements are still being disproven, in science at any rate.

Helium

Helium derives its name from the Greek word "Helios," meaning the sun. This element has long been recognized as a constituent of the solar atmosphere, having been discovered there by spectroscopic observations prior to its isolation in the laboratory by Ramsay and Kaiser in 1895. More recently it has been identified as a minor component of the air, to the extent of one part in 200,000 parts of air; it is thus scarcer than neon, but more plentiful than krypton or xenon in the air. Although helium is an atmospheric gas, it is the first of the gases considered in this chapter which is not prepared commercially by air separation (although minor amounts can be and are obtained this way). Most commercial helium is obtained by low-temperature separation from natural gas.

Helium is the coldest of the cryogenic fluids, liquefying at $-269°C$, only $4°C$ above absolute zero. Further cooling will not produce solid helium at atmospheric pressure, since the solid can be obtained only at higher pressures. They depend upon the temperature; the equilibrium pressure of solid helium at absolute zero has been calculated to be 25 atmospheres.

The history of helium in cryogenics dates from about 1947 when the first commercial helium liquefier was developed. Prior to World War II, there were only about a dozen laboratories in the world equipped with helium liquefiers (See Chapter 4 and Figure 4-1).

As noted above, all helium produced commercially is separated by high-pressure cryogenic methods. Originally, the major use of helium was for the inflation of lighter-than-air craft. This application was important before and during World War II, but has decreased due to the virtual disappearance of the so-called "blimps." Helium is used today (See Figure 1-8) in:

— balloons for weather observation, cosmic ray studies, astronomical and other scientific observations.
— inert protective atmospheres for welding and metallurgical processing.
— rockets and missiles
— atomic energy installations.
— airplane tires. Filling the tires of a Boeing 707 with helium instead of air saves the weight of one passenger
— oxygen-helium mixtures for deep-sea diving or for treatment of pulmonary edemas.
— hypersonic wind tunnels, as a working fluid.

For divers, the use of helium-air mixtures avoids nitrogen narcosis—the adverse effect of dissolved nitrogen in the blood on

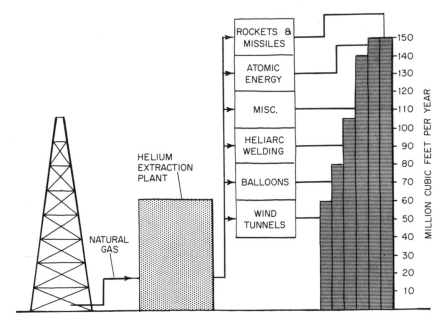

Fig. 1-8   Helium — sources and uses in the U. S. A.

the nervous system. In the treatment of pulmonary edemas the helium diffuses rapidly past lung blockages and secretions, carrying the oxygen with it.

All helium produced in the United States is sold by the U.S. Bureau of Mines, in view of the strategic nature and limited availability of this gas. Once separated only in plants owned and operated by the Bureau of Mines and shipped in multicylinder cars as a gas (See Figure 1-9), it is now being purchased from

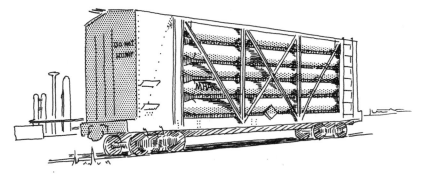

FIG. 1-9   Typical high pressure gas freight car for helium.

private industry as well, under an expanded government production program aimed at conservation of United States helium resources.

Hydrogen

Hydrogen, as well as helium, is a useful cryogenic fluid in the extremely low temperature range, a few degrees above absolute zero. Hydrogen becomes liquid at —253°C (—423°F) and solidifies at —259°C (—434°F). It is an unusual fluid because of its low density, which is only about $\frac{1}{4}$ that of water.

Hydrogen, unlike the other cryogenic gases discussed so far in this chapter, is not produced by cryogenic means. The major raw material is natural gas, which consists chiefly of methane. In one process, the methane is reacted with steam

$$CH_4 + 2H_2O \rightarrow CO_2 + 4H_2$$

the carbon dioxide being removed by scrubbing with an absorbent solution. In another process the methane is reacted with steam and oxygen

$$2CH_4 + O_2 + 2H_2O \rightarrow 2CO_2 + 6H_2$$

the carbon dioxide again being removed by scrubbing.

Both these processes yield hydrogen in the gaseous state, as contrasted with the cryogenic processes for separating the gases in air, which yield them as liquids. Therefore, hydrogen is liquefied only when required in that form for specific applications. Most liquid hydrogen produced is for end use as a rocket fuel. In the chemical rockets which operate on fuel (propellant) and liquid oxygen, hydrogen is the favored propellant because its low density results in higher velocities of the exhaust gases as they emerge from the rocket nozzles. These higher velocities produce more thrust for a given rate of consumption of propellant. (For rocket diagram, see Figure 1-10). The advantages of hydrogen as a rocket

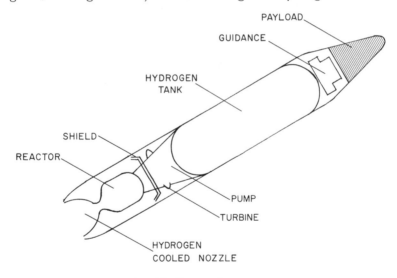

FIG. 1-10 Nuclear rocket components

fuel account largely for the rapid growth of liquid hydrogen capacity in the United States (See Figure 1-11). They also would seem to promise a solid future for liquid hydrogen, in spite of the dynamic nature of the propellant field, and the rapid changes that occur in it.

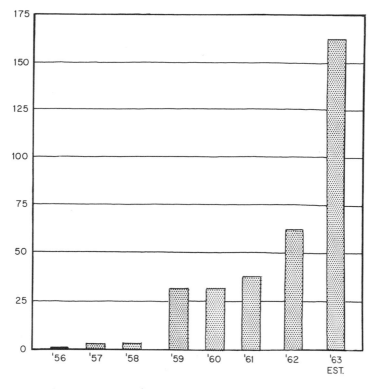

FIG. 1-11   U. S. liquid hydrogen capacity (tons/day).

The first hydrogen bomb depended on liquid hydrogen for its operation. Thus some of the original impetus for hydrogen research came from the Atomic Energy Commission. More recently, heavy hydrogen or deuterium has been combined with the lithium isotope, lithium-6, to give lithium-6 deuteride as a thermonuclear explosive. If peacetime thermonuclear reactors become an economic reality they will depend on deuterium or tritium as fuels. The deuterium may well be obtained by a cryogenic separation as is discussed in Chapter 9 (See Figure 9-8).

Thus the cryogenic uses of hydrogen — in chemical and in nuclear rockets, as well as in fusion reaction devices — involves the wedding of hot and cold — of super-high temperatures with super-cold temperatures to produce super-power.

Methane

Most of the cryogenic gases mentioned above have proven to be useful cryogenic fluids in various industrial processes. Methane is not as useful in cryogenics as the others, but cryogenics may provide the key to large scale transport and use of methane.

Methane liquefies at $-162°C$ ($-260°F$) and becomes solid at $-184°C$ ($-299°F$). Available in huge quantities in natural gas, it has, of course, been transported overland by pipeline, but overseas shipment or storage of huge quantities in gaseous form appears to be prohibitively expensive. Therefore, systems have been developed for the liquefaction of methane, and shipment and storage of the liquid. Such systems are already in commercial use, and appear to have a great future. Shipment of liquid methane from

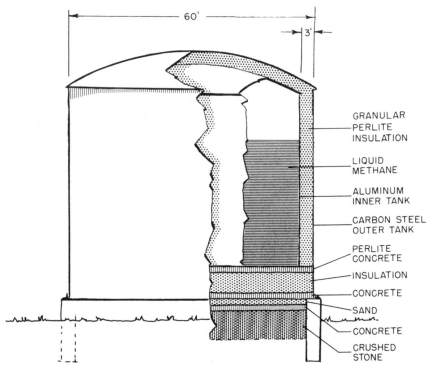

FIG. 1-12   Large liquid methane storage tank.

gas-producing areas to England and Japan could each become $100 million ventures. Storage of natural gas in liquid form during the summer could help to level out the uneconomic consumption pattern of natural gas, for which winter demand reaches a peak and summer use falls to a very low level. Figure 1-12 shows a typical large liquid methane storage installation.

Ethylene

Cryogenic techniques are utilized in the separation of ethylene from mixtures of cracked hydrocarbon gases; most of the billions of pounds of ethylene produced in the United States today are produced by low-temperature separation techniques (See Figure 1-13).

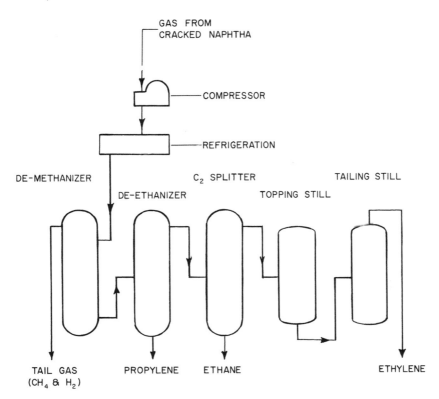

Fig. 1-13   Ethylene separation at low temperature.

Ethylene is somewhat unique among the hydrocarbon gases in that it is also used as a low-temperature refrigerant. In fact, boiling liquid ethylene is used as the coolant in the only large-scale synthetic organic chemical process which is operated at cryogenic temperatures — the manufacture of butyl rubber at $-100°C$ ($-148°F$.) (See Figure 1-14).

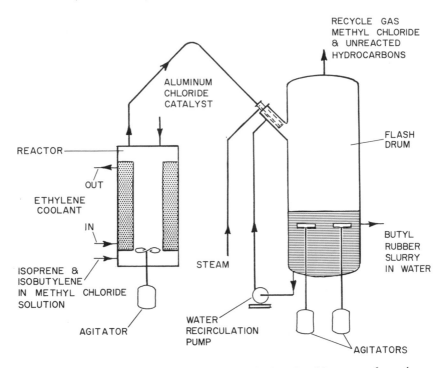

FIG. 1-14 Ethylene as cryogenic coolant in butyl rubber manufacturing.

Ethylene liquefies at $-104°C$ ($-155°F$) and if cooled further can solidify at $-169°C$ ($-272°F$).

Fluorine

Fluorine might be called an impractical cryogenic fluid. Unlike all the cryogenic gases mentioned up to this point, fluorine is a violently reactive and corrosive material. It is really only worthy of mention here because liquid fluorine is an industrial commodity and its production and transport involve cryogenics (See Figure 1-15). With a boiling point of —188°C (—306°F), it falls squarely into the cryogenic category between oxygen and nitrogen. Since, because of its reactive chemical properties, it is not a useful cryogenic fluid, it is not discussed at length in this book.

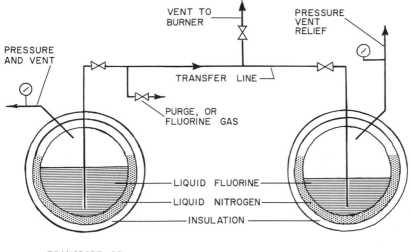

FIG. 1-15   Liquid fluorine transfer system.

Chapter 2

HOW COLD IS PRODUCED

The production of cold, in the sense in which the term is used in this book, involves the production of liquefied gases. Michael Faraday attempted to obtain liquefied gases by compressing hydrogen, methane, etc., but he had no success, as the temperatures were too high to permit liquefaction of the gases at the pressures he was using.

The first landmark in temperature reduction was the discovery of the Joule-Thomson effect as a result of the so-called porous plug experiment in 1853.

It remained for Thomas Andrews to discover in 1869 that low temperature was the key to the liquefaction of carbon dioxide. He discovered the principle of the critical temperature, above which a gas cannot be liquefied, regardless of the pressure to which it is subjected. Prior to realization of the significance of this principle, the nitrogen and oxygen of the air, as well as other gases such as hydrogen, were regarded as "permanent" gases — i.e., substances permanently in the gaseous state which could not be liquefied.

In 1877 Louis-Paul Cailletet in France and Raoul Pictet in Geneva liquefied oxygen. Cailletet observed a mist of droplets in his apparatus when compressed oxygen at $-30°C$ was suddenly expanded. Pictet actually produced a jet of liquid oxygen. These investigators were observant and fortunate, but the science of that day was not sophisticated enough to permit them to go beyond the bare observations. In fact, Cailletet was under the impression that he obtained liquid hydrogen when he repeated his experiment with hydrogen; we know now that this could not have been the case. In a real sense, however, these men opened the door to cryogenic miracles of today.

In April of 1883, Sigmund von Wroblewski and Karl Olszewski obtained first oxygen and then nitrogen in a discrete liquid state with a clearly recognizable meniscus. This work was done at the University of Cracow in Poland.

Having thus progressed to the —185°C (—300°F) level of liquid oxygen and nitrogen, the next goal set by scientists was the attainment of the —250°C (—418°F) range represented by liquid hydrogen. Wroblewski cooled hydrogen in a capillary to liquid oxygen temperatures and then suddenly expanded it from 100 atmospheres to one atmosphere. He obtained a fog which might be considered a counterpart of Cailletet's "oxygen mist" in 1884. It was not until 1898, however, that Dewar obtained hydrogen as a visible liquid body, boiling in a test tube.

Then in 1902, Claude pioneered the use of the expansion engine for the production of very low temperatures. This was the second landmark in the history of temperature reduction (the first having been the discovery of the Joule-Thomson effect in 1853). Then came the liquefaction of helium by Onnes in 1908 — an achievement whereby the last of the known gases was obtained in the liquid state. The third landmark in temperature reduction was the suggestion of the magnetic method of cooling by Debye and Giauque in 1926. This last advance permitted a very close approach to the limiting temperature of absolute zero.

PHASE CHANGES

One of the simplest methods of cooling a body of liquid is by induced evaporation (See Figure 2-1). The gas liquefies in the left hand vessel when it is cooled in the compressed state. The compressed liquid is forced through the throttling valve into the low pressure coil at the right where it "flashes" into a vapor and cools the brine. The heat of vaporization represents the amount

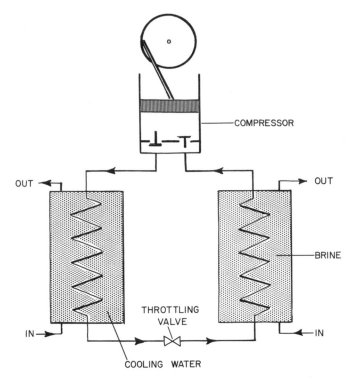

FIG. 2-1   The elements of refrigeration due to phase change.

of refrigeration which is available. This technique is an ancient one. It dates back to the use of porous vessels for keeping liquids cool. The first recorded mechanical ice-making machine, which was built by Cullen in 1755, was based on the principle of cooling by evaporation. This technique is now used in commercial and household refrigerators, but is generally not applied to the production of cryogenic temperatures. However helium, which boils at 4° Kelvin, may be boiled under reduced pressure to give temperatures down to 1° Kelvin.*

The controlled pumping of a gas from an adsorbent material is another example of refrigeration by phase change; the heat of adsorption is analogous to the heat of evaporation in ordinary

---

* On the Kelvin temperature scale, the degree is the same as on the Centigrade scale, but the zero point is absolute zero, so that 0°K = −273.16°C.

evaporation. If helium gas is adsorbed on charcoal at the temperature of 12°K, the sublimation temperature of solid hydrogen at
reduced pressure, controlled desorption of the helium may be
used to produce temperatures in the range of 5 to 12°K.

An early and classical application of the principle of phase
change to the attainment of liquid air temperatures was the
cascade system shown in Figure 2-2. The origination of this

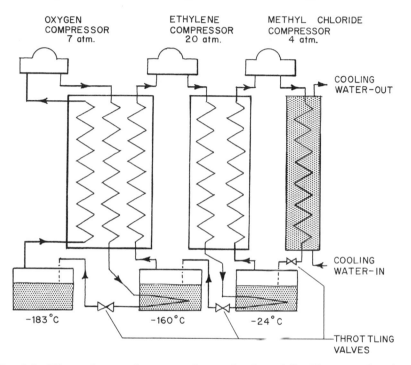

FIG. 2-2   The early cascade process for production of liquid oxygen by phase
change.

cascade scheme is attributed to Pictet. In the cascade process, a
series of liquids of progressively lower boiling points are condensed — each under pressure and at the temperature produced
by the evaporation of the next higher boiling liquid.

JOULE-THOMSON EFFECT

The cooling phenomenon which occurs when a gas under pressure is forced past a constriction was first observed in 1853 by James Prescott Joule and also by William Thomson, who later became Lord Kelvin. The effect, which we now know as the Joule-Thomson effect, can be produced by the passage of the high-pressure gas through a partially-opened valve, a very small orifice or a porous plug. The discovery of this effect made possible such practical applications of cryogenics as the volume production of liquid air, and then the first liquefaction of hydrogen and that of helium. The principle of the Joule-Thomson effect is shown in Figure 2-3. A laboratory apparatus which demonstrates this effect is illustrated in Figure 2-4. As the air flows through the nozzle, it cools. This cooler air then flows

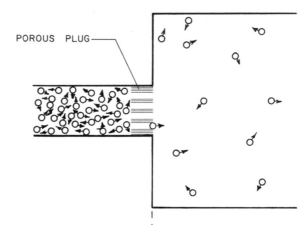

FIG. 2-3   Principle of Joule-Thomson effect.

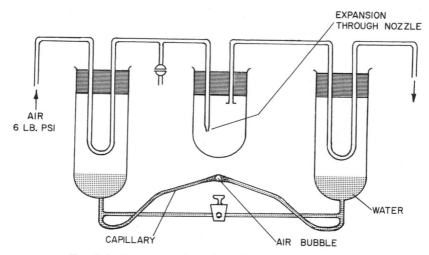

FIG. 2-4 Demonstration of Joule-Thomson effect.

through the tube in the vessel at the right, cooling the air in that vessel and causing it to contract, so that the bubble in the capillary moves to the right.

This effect is sometimes called the Joule-Kelvin effect since William Thomson later became Lord Kelvin. Its fundamental principle is that of using "internal work" to cool a gas. This work results from the fact that the molecules separate further as the gas expands. In separating, they are moving against the Van der Waals force of attraction between them; the energy for this motion is obtained at the expense of their kinetic energy. The loss in kinetic energy results in a decrease in internal energy of the gas and a drop in temperature.

It is interesting to recall that Joule had concluded, prior to his discovery of the Joule-Thomson effect, that a gas which obeys Boyle's law perfectly could not exhibit this effect. His conclusion was sound, but at that time he did not know that no real gas obeys Boyle's law perfectly, for two reasons. The first is the attraction between molecules which, as explained above, causes the cooling of a gas during a Joule-Thomson expansion. The second reason why real gases do not obey Boyle's law perfectly is because that law assumes that molecules are dimensionless points, and thus disregards their volume. The effect of the volume of the molecules is to cause the gas to heat instead of cooling during a Joule-Thomson expansion. Thus the net temperature effect of the expansion is the resultant of two processes, one that tends to cool the gas and another that tends to heat it. Since the changes in the two processes with temperature is not the same, there is an inversion temperature at which the Joule-Thomson effect is zero — below this temperature the gas cools on Joule-Thomson expansion, while above the inversion temperature it heats. At room temperature, hydrogen and helium are above their inversion temperatures and warm when expanded; all other common gases are cooled by expansion at room temperature and below it.

EXPANSION ENGINES

The Joule-Thomson effect is concerned, as stated above, with expansions of gases which take place without doing external work. Now consider that when a gas is enclosed in a cylinder (or any other rigid container) the molecules rebound from the walls with unchanged speed and the condition of the gas remains the same. If however, the cylinder is fitted with a piston which moves and allows the gas volume to increase, the molecules rebound with a lower velocity. The resulting loss of energy of the molecules results in a fall of the temperature of the gas.

The use of an expansion engine to remove heat as mechanical work was the next step after the Joule-Thomson effect on the road to economic production of liquefied gases for cryogenic applications. This step was first taken by the Frenchman, George Claude, in 1902 (See Figure 2-5).

The extension of this basic principle to the use of a turbine rather than an engine is attributed to Peter Kapitsa at about 1939. He applied his apparatus to the liquefaction of helium.

One widespread application of the expansion engine to helium liquefaction has been the Collins Cryostat, the laboratory device for producing liquid helium which is known the world over (See Figure 3-4).

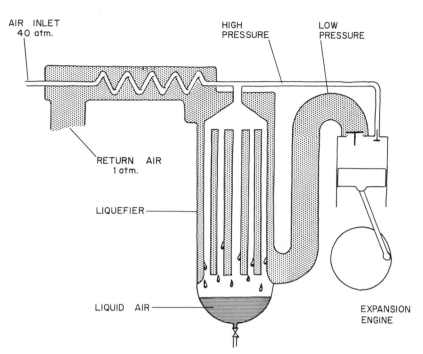

AIR   INLET
40 atm.

HIGH
PRESSURE

LOW
PRESSURE

RETURN   AIR
1 atm.

LIQUEFIER

LIQUID   AIR

EXPANSION
ENGINE

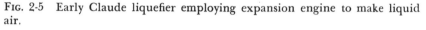

FIG. 2-5   Early Claude liquefier employing expansion engine to make liquid
air.

MAGNETIC EFFECTS

As mentioned above, boiling liquid helium has a temperature
of 4° Kelvin. Boiling liquid helium at reduced pressures can give
temperatures down to 1° Kelvin but below that, one cannot go
by such methods. Since there is no gas with a boiling point
lower than helium, production of temperatures below 1° Kelvin,
that is, within 1° of absolute zero, requires an entirely different
technique, such as that of adiabatic demagnetization.

Adiabatic demagnetization is based on the fact that paramagnetic salts, such as iron alum and chrome alum, contains atoms
which behave like small magnets. Under ordinary conditions,
these atoms lie at random angles to one another. When such
a material is subjected to a powerful magnetic field, the magnets
are aligned and heat is produced in the process. In the cryogenic

application of adiabatic demagnetization, the material or system under study is cooled as far as possible (to about 1°K) by the use of helium. It is then magnetized, and the heat of magnetization removed by the helium cooling system, so it is again at 1°K, and within the magnetic field. The field is then removed, and the atoms in demagnetizing absorb heat equal to the heat of magnetization, thus cooling the system below 1°K. (See Figure 2-6).

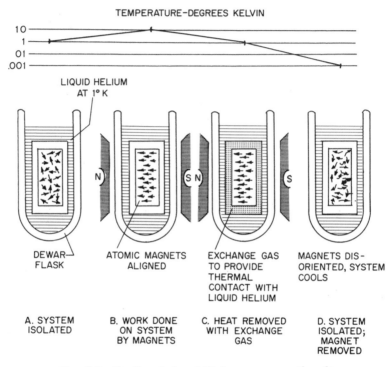

Fig. 2-6   Cooling below 1°K by paramagnetic salts.

Chapter 3

THE GREAT NAMES IN COLD

In the last chapter, we mentioned some of the important names in the history of cold. In this chapter, we present the national and educational backgrounds of some of the great names in cold — since cryogenics, like all other branches of science and technology, is based on the contributions of a number of outstanding individuals.

WILLIAM THOMSON, LORD KELVIN

The absolute scale of temperature was the contribution to cryogenics of William Thomson, who was born in 1824 of a Scottish family. His birthplace was Belfast in Northern Ireland but was educated at the University of Glasgow in Scotland. After further study at Cambridge and Paris, he returned to Glasgow to become a professor of physics in 1846 at the age of 22. In 1847, he met James Prescott Joule and their discussions of the nature of heat resulted in Thomson's proposing his absolute scale of temperatures in 1848.

In 1853, Thomson devised his classic porous plug experiment which he carried out in conjunction with Joule. Figure 3-1 shows an early Joule-Thomson liquefier.

When only 34 years of age, he was knighted as Sir William Thomson for the part he had played in the laying of the first Atlantic cable. When he was 68 years old and had been teaching

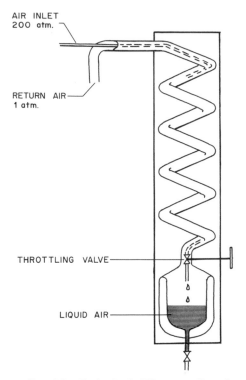

AIR INLET
200 atm.

RETURN AIR
1 atm.

THROTTLING VALVE

LIQUID AIR

FIG. 3-1   Early Joule-Thomson liquefier.

at Glasgow for 46 years, he was made a Lord by Queen Victoria. He chose the title Lord Kelvin after the River Kelvin which flows past the campus of the University of Glasgow. He died in 1907 and is buried in Westminster Abbey.

JAMES DEWAR

The idea of using vacuum jacketed vessels for the storage of cryogenic fluids was originated in 1892 by James Dewar, after whom the Dewar flask or simply "the Dewar" has been named (See Figure 3-2). Such containers are also well-known in the household under the name of "Thermos" bottles.

Dewar was born at Kincardine-on-Forth in Scotland in 1842. He was educated in chemistry at the University of Edinburgh

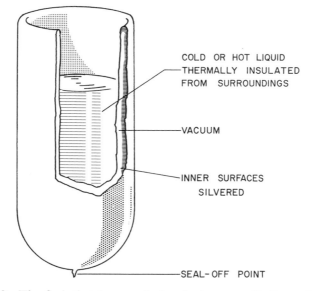

COLD OR HOT LIQUID
THERMALLY INSULATED
FROM SURROUNDINGS

VACUUM

INNER SURFACES
SILVERED

SEAL-OFF POINT

FIG. 3-2 The flask that is named after its inventor, Sir James Dewar.

and later studied at Ghent in Belgium under Frederick Kekulé, the man who first developed the concept of the hexagonal ring structure of benzene. He was made a Professor at Cambridge in 1875 and also accepted an endowed chair at the Royal Institution in London in 1877.

Dewar was an extremely versatile scientist, working in such diverse fields as organic chemistry, spectroscopy and explosives. His work in cryogenics dates from 1874, when he published a paper on the latent heat of liquid gases. Stimulated by reports of the Frenchmen, Cailletet and Pictet, and of the Poles, Wroblewski and Olszewski, he constructed a machine for producing liquid oxygen in quantity in 1891. In 1892, he invented the Dewar flask. In 1898, he was the first to liquefy hydrogen, and in 1899 he made solid hydrogen for the first time. He was knighted in 1904 for his scientific accomplishments, and died in 1923.

FRANZ EUGEN SIMON

Simon was the founder of the laboratory for low temperature research at the Clarendon Laboratory at Oxford University. He was born in Berlin in 1893. He studied there at the Institut fur Physikalische Chemie.

He was originally a pupil of Walter Nernst, the great German thermodynamicist, and did low-temperature work both at Breslau and at Berlin. In 1927, he devised the first simple method for producing liquid helium for experimental purposes. His apparatus is shown in Figure 3-3. It harked back in principle to Cailletet's first process for liquid oxygen in that only a single adiabatic expansion was used; Simon, however, conducted his expansion at liquid hydrogen temperatures.

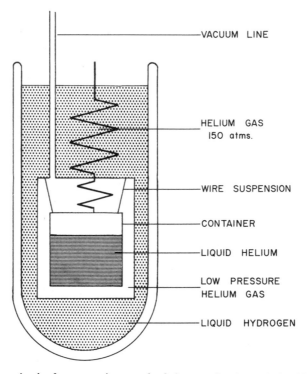

FIG. 3-3 Simon's single expansion method for production of liquid helium.

He left Germany in 1933 after the start of the Hitler regime and went to England where he established the nucleus of the low temperature research group at Oxford, along with his former students, Mendelssohn and Kurti. During World War II, he worked in Canada and was largely responsible for the diffusion method of separating the isotope, uranium-235, which was applied on a large scale at Oak Ridge, Tennessee. After the war, he re-entered low temperature work in the new Clarendon Laboratory at Oxford. He was knighted Sir Francis Simon in 1954. He died in 1956, barely a month after assuming a new appointment as professor of experimental philosophy and head of the Clarendon Laboratory.

HEIKE KAMERLINGH ONNES

The first liquefaction of helium and the discovery of superconductivity are both credited to Kamerlingh Onnes and the workers in his laboratory at the University of Leiden.

Onnes was born in 1853 at Groningen in the Netherlands. He became a student at the University of Groningen in 1870. From 1871 to 1873 he worked under Bunsen and Kirchhoff at Heidelberg, returning to Groningen where he remained until 1878.

He was appointed Professor of Physics at the University of Leiden in 1882. In 1894 he prepared the plan for the equipment and operation of the low-temperature laboratories there. By 1904 he had produced liquid air on a large scale; by 1906 he had prepared liquid hydrogen in quantity.

His first production of liquid helium, in 1908, was a tribute both to his skill and his patience. The helium gas was obtained by heating monazite sand from India; it has been estimated that the volume of gas needed to make a liter of liquid helium would cost $65,000 if the work of Onnes were to be repeated today. In its way, that first liter of helium was as priceless as the first gram of radium extracted by the Curies. In 1913 he received the Nobel Prize for his accomplishments in liquefying helium and for his subsequent research at low temperatures. He was made an honorary member of practically every learned society in the world. Aside from helium liquefaction, his most notable contribution was in discovery of the phenomenon of superconductivity. Onnes died in 1926.

CARL VON LINDE

Von Linde was not the first man to liquefy air, but he was the first to realize the industrial implications of gas liquefaction and to put these ideas into practice. Born in 1824 in Austria, Von Linde studied at the Polytechnic Institute in Zurich from 1861 to 1864. In 1868 at the age of 26, he became a professor at the Technische Hochschule in Munich; from 1868 to 1879 he taught the theory of refrigeration and the design of refrigeration machines — giving the first courses in these subjects ever to be presented.

He invented the ammonia refrigeration machine, which was patented in 1870. His first successful commercial refrigeration machine was built in Trieste in 1877 and operated successfully for 31 years, producing ice for a brewery. In 1879 he founded the company, Linde's Eismaschinen AG, which bears his name to this day. In the 1880's he turned to engineering research on air liquefaction and separation, retiring from the chairmanship of the company in 1891. He was granted a basic patent on air liquefaction in Germany in 1895. In 1910 he developed the modern double column which is now used almost universally for air separation. In 1925, at the age of 83, he successfully applied refrigeration to the separation of coke oven gas into its constituents. Von Linde died in 1934 at the age of 92.

GEORGES CLAUDE

Claude, who was born in 1870 in Paris, was the first to point out that expansion in an engine is a more efficient way to remove energy from a compressed gas than is expansion through a valve. Claude received his education at the École de Physique et de Chimie.

In 1896 he became interested in acetylene and developed a technique for handling acetylene in solution for welding. His studies on acetylene led him to work on cheaper methods of making calcium carbide as a source of acetylene, one of which was the combustion of a mixture of coal and lime in oxygen. For this purpose he needed pure oxygen, which led him to study liquid air. In 1902, he developed a practical cycle for air liquefaction in which most of the cooling was effected in a reciprocating expansion engine; just enough cooling was done by Joule-Thomson expansion to avoid producing liquid in the engine. In that same year, 1902, the French company, L'Air Liquide, was founded to develop and commercialize the Claude patents.

In 1907 Claude separated helium and neon in quantity from the air. In 1910 he invented the neon lamp and did research on the use of oxygen in steel manufacture. In 1917 he devised a high-pressure process, which bears his name, for the synthesis of ammonia from the elements.

In the latter years of his life, Claude worked on the utilization of temperature differences in the sea water at various depths; his intent was to devise a practical power generator using heat from sea water to generate and condense steam under vacuum. Claude died on May 23, 1960 at the age of 90.

WILLIAM FRANCIS GIAUQUE

Giauque was the co-discoverer, with Debye, of adiabatic demagnetization as applied in the use of paramagnetic salts to achieve temperatures below 1°K. He was born at Niagara Falls, Ontario, in 1895. He was educated at the Niagara Falls Collegiate Institute and at the University of California at Berkeley.

His work on cryogenics which resulted in the award to him of the Nobel Prize in Chemistry in 1949 was performed independently of — and almost simultaneously with — that of Debye, who was to share the Nobel Prize with him. It was in 1926 that he proposed the adiabatic demagnetization method for attaining temperatures below one degree absolute. The first successful experiments making use of this technique were performed by Giauque and MacDougall at Berkeley in 1933, closely followed by De Haas and his co-workers at the Kamerlingh Onnes Laboratory at Leiden in the Netherlands, and by Kurti and Simon at the Clarendon Laboratory at Oxford in 1934.

PETER JOSEPH WILHELM DEBYE

Debye was the co-discoverer with Giauque of adiabatic demagnetization. He was born in 1884 in the Netherlands. After working at various European universities, he came to the United States in 1940. His many contributions to science are clearly evident from the number of principles and phenomena that bear his name, such as the Debye-Huckel Limiting Law, the Debye Temperature, the Debye-Sears Effect, the Debye-Huckel of Specific Heat, and many others. He is now a professor of physical chemistry at Cornell University in Ithaca, New York.

PETER KAPITSA

Peter Leonidovich Kapitsa was born in 1894. He graduated from the Petrograd Polytechnical Institute in 1918. In 1921 he went to England and worked there under the physicist, Ernest Rutherford. In 1924 he was appointed deputy director of the Cavendish Magnetic Research Laboratory. In 1929 he was elected a fellow of the British Royal Society as well as a corresponding member of the Academy of Sciences of the USSR. About this time, Kapitsa refused several offers to return to the Soviet Union and work there; in 1934 he did accept an invitation to tour the Soviet Union and visit physicists there, with the guarantee of a free return to England. Upon arrival he was forbidden to return to England; he protested and, indeed, refused to work for an entire year. He finally capitulated, however, and was made director of the Institute of Physical Problems of the USSR in 1936. He applied the expansion turbine to gas liquefaction in 1939 and in the same year was made a full member of the Academy of Sciences of the USSR. In 1941 he was awarded a Stalin Prize for developing the turboexpander and applying it to air liquefaction. In 1943 he won another Stalin Prize for his work on heat transfer and superfluidity in helium II

In 1945 Kapitsa resisted efforts of the Soviet government to make him confine his studies to high energy physics and nuclear weapons. He was removed from his job and imprisoned. Since Stalin's death, he has been returned to his old post, but is reported to supervise laboratories and experimental projects dealing with nuclear and thermonuclear weapons.

SAMUEL CORNETTE COLLINS

Samuel Cornette Collins was born in Democrat, Kentucky on September 28, 1898. He received his undergraduate education at the University of Tennessee, and his Ph.D. in chemistry at the University of North Carolina in Chapel Hill. After teaching at the Universities of Tennessee and North Carolina, he went to Massachusetts Institute of Technology in 1930 as a research associate. He became an assistant professor in 1936, an associate professor in 1941, and in 1949 he was named a full Professor of Cryogenic Engineering in the Department of Mechanical Engineering.

During World War II, Professor Collins was a technical aide to the National Defense Research Council at Wright Field in Dayton, Ohio. There he helped to develop low-pressure, lightweight oxygen generators for aircraft use.

He invented the famous Collins Cryostat in 1947 (See Figure 3-4). In 1958 he was awarded the Kamerlingh Onnes gold medal of the Dutch Society for Refrigeration. In the preceding 50 years the Society had awarded only two silver medals. This was the first gold medal and the first award to any American. His areas of research specialization have been the thermodynamic properties of gases, the production and maintenance of very low temperatures, and the improvement of oxygen processes of the low-pressure type.

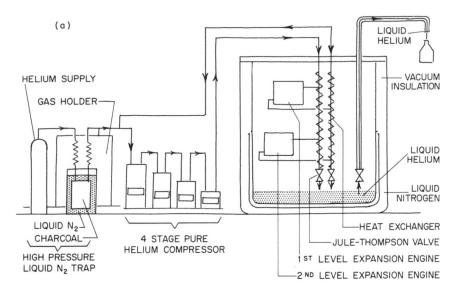

(a)

HELIUM SUPPLY

GAS HOLDER

LIQUID HELIUM

VACUUM INSULATION

LIQUID HELIUM

LIQUID NITROGEN

LIQUID N₂
CHARCOAL
HIGH PRESSURE
LIQUID N₂ TRAP

4 STAGE PURE
HELIUM COMPRESSOR

HEAT EXCHANGER
JULE-THOMPSON VALVE
1ST LEVEL EXPANSION ENGINE
2ND LEVEL EXPANSION ENGINE

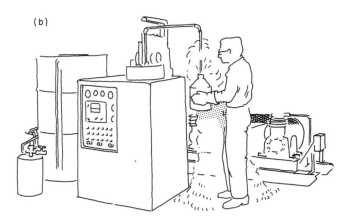

(b)

FIG. 3-4   Collins helium cryostat (a) Diagram; (b) Typical installation.

Chapter 4

WHERE COLD IS STUDIED

As with most other divisions of science, research in cryogenics is divided between university, government, and industrial laboratories. In these three categories, there are a number of important research centers in the world today.

If we consider the attainment of liquid helium temperatures as the criterion for a "cryogenic laboratory," we would define the Kamerlingh Onnes Laboratory at the University of Leiden as the world's first, dating from 1908. That laboratory was alone in this field of research until 1923, when it was joined by the laboratory of the University of Toronto in Canada. By 1939 there were 11 such laboratories — 4 in the United States, 3 in Great Britain and one each in Holland, Canada, the USSR and Germany. By 1946, it has been estimated that there were 15 such laboratories around the world; by 1961 the number had increased to over 600, representing every country in the world. Much of this growth (See Figure 4-1) can be attributed to the availability of the Collins cryostat.

KAMERLINGH ONNES LABORATORY — LEIDEN

This laboratory was founded in 1885 by Kamerlingh Onnes at the University of Leiden in Holland, following his appointment to the faculty there in 1882.

A cascade apparatus, modeled after that of Pictet and using a a methyl chloride, ethylene, oxygen sequence (See Figure 2-2) was

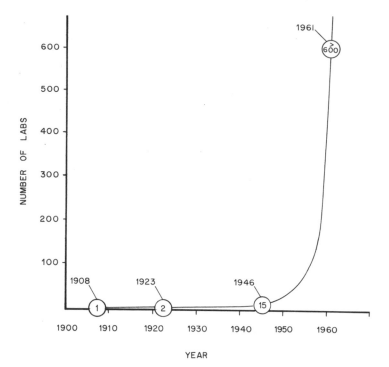

FIG. 4-1 Growth in number of laboratories capable of research at liquid helium temperatures.

a significant piece of original equipment. It was supplemented by an apparatus for preparing 14 liters of liquid air per hour. There was also a plant for the production of liquid hydrogen at the rate of 13 liters per hour. In 1922 equipment was provided for the production of both liquid helium and liquid neon.

As of 1962, the laboratory personnel consisted of 175 graduate students, technicians and professional staff members. A new building addition of four stories having 2 basements is under construction with occupancy planned for early 1964; this will double the available laboratory space. Current research deals with refinement of temperature scales for use in cryogenic ranges, as well as with precise measurement of physical properties of gases, liquids and solids at very low temperatures. Magnets are available for the production of 60,000 gauss continuous fields and also for 500,000 gauss fields in short (20 millisecond) pulses.

CLARENDON LABORATORY — OXFORD

The Clarendon Laboratory is the physics department of the University of Oxford and embraces both teaching and research. It produces about one-sixth of all the honors graduates in physics in Great Britain.

The original Clarendon Laboratory was built in 1872 and derived its name from the fact that it was financed from the sale of the Earl of Clarendon's "History of the Great Rebellion." The money was left in 1751 in a fund for the establishment of a riding academy at Oxford. In 1861 the money was still unspent and the trustees of the estate, "by that wisdom which belongs only to lawyers and trustees," decided to forego the riding school which was not needed in favor of a laboratory for physical sciences which was badly needed indeed. That early building now houses the Department of Geology at Oxford, and the present Clarendon Laboratory buildings date from 1910 (the Townsend Building), 1939 (the Lindemann Building) and 1947 (the Simon Building). The low temperature research center dates from about 1933.

Professor B. Bleaney has been in charge of the Clarendon Laboratory since 1957, following the retirement of the late Professor Lord Cherwell — formerly Professor Lindemann — and the untimely death of Professor Sir Francis Simon in 1956.

Of the 150 research workers on the staff of the Clarendon Laboratory today, about 40 are engaged in low temperature work and consitute one of the top cryogenic research groups in the world today. These research workers are assisted by a technical staff numbering about 60.

A helium liquefier with a capacity of 12 liters per hour built in 1956 and a hydrogen liquefier with a capacity of 18 liters per hour built in 1953 supply some 30 cryostats with about 50 liters per week of liquid helium and 300 liters of liquid hydrogen. About 2 tons per week of liquid nitrogen is purchased from the British Oxygen Company.

Much of the work in the Clarendon Laboratory is concerned with the properties of pure metals at liquid helium temperatures.

Strength and fatigue properties are studied with the goal of establishing a fundamental theory of the fatigue process. Other work includes studies of the fundamental properties of liquid helium, studies of the atomic nucleus at low temperatures, and studies of the magnetic properties, as well as the solid-state properties of materials.

ROYAL SOCIETY MOND LABORATORY — CAMBRIDGE

The Royal Society Mond Laboratory was established by Kapitsa and Cockcroft at Cambridge at about the same time that Simon was establishing the low-temperature group at Oxford. The initial complement comprised apparatus for producing intense magnetic fields as well as a plant for cryogenic work. The latter included a hydrogen liquefier which was unique in that it was designed to liquefy hydrogen of a lower degree of purity than that generally used for the purpose. The production rate of this liquefier was 4 liters per hour.

Currently there are six members of the teaching staff engaged in low-temperature work, in addition to three or four research fellows or senior visitors and about 20 candidates for the Ph.D. degree.

A Joule-Thomson helium liquefier with an output of 4 liters per hour provides liquid helium; the older hydrogen liquefier is now rarely used. Temperatures below 1°K can be produced by magnetic cooling and by a cryostat using helium-3. There is available equipment to produce steady magnetic fields of 60 kilogauss intensity and pulsed fields of 200 kilogauss.

Most of the work of the Mond Laboratory today is concerned with the behavior of electrons in metals, especially the study of Fermi surfaces and superconductivity.

LABORATORIES IN THE U.S.S.R.

In the Soviet Union, there are two cryogenic laboratories in Moscow, one at the Academy of Sciences and the second at

Moscow University. Outside of Moscow there is a long-established laboratory in Kharkov, at the Physical Institute of the Ukrainian Academy of Sciences, plus at least two major new laboratories, one at Tiflis (Tbilisi), the capital of the Georgian Soviet Republic, and the other at Sverdlovsk in the Urals.

Kapitsa is the Director of the Institute for Physical Problems of the Academy of Sciences and is responsible for overall direction of low temperature research, although he has not devoted his personal energies to this field in the last several years.

A great amount of Soviet research effort is devoted to liquid helium studies. Other areas of research concentration include superconductivity and magnetic properties at low temperatures, as well as studies of the Fermi surfaces in metals.

At the University of Moscow, an undergraduate course in cryogenics is taught, including some ten experiments with liquid helium, and an experiment on adiabatic demagnetization.

MacLENNON LABORATORIES — TORONTO

Sir John Cunningham MacLennon was responsible for the first liquefaction of helium in Canada about 1922, which was the first development outside of Holland in the wake of Onnes' pioneering discovery at Leiden in 1908. Born in 1867 and until his death in 1935 one of Canada's outstanding physicists, MacLennon built up the laboratory at the University of Toronto which bears his name.

Current areas of research interest include properties of liquid helium; thermal and electrical properties of superconductors, dilute alloys, and high purity metals, and specific heats of condensed gases.

NATIONAL RESEARCH COUNCIL — OTTAWA

The laboratory of low temperature and solid state physics at the National Research Council in Ottawa was founded in 1951. The founder was Dr. David Keith Chalmers MacDonald who came from England to start the laboratory. The staff grew from one to 15 scientists in the 10 years from 1951 to 1961. Under Dr. MacDonald, there are now 10 regular staff members and 7 postdoctoral fellows.

The low temperature group at Ottawa has made important contributions in the field of electrical resistance at low temperatures and has also done significant work on specific heats, on atomic spacings in crystals, and in semiconductor physics.

LINDE COMPANY

The Linde Company is a division of Union Carbide Corporation. Its cryogenic research facilities are divided between Tonawanda, New York and Indianapolis, Indiana; the Speedway Research Laboratories at Indianapolis is a newer and smaller unit. A technical center at Roseland, New Jersey, just west of New York City, is in the planning stage.

At Tonawanda there are over 150 professionally-trained people, plus about 200 in the supporting staff of technicians and administrators, all of whom are engaged in research and development activities. This is exclusive of an engineering and construction organization devoted to the design and manufacture of air separation plants and miscellaneous cryogenic equipment.

At Speedway there are about 20 professionally trained people, plus about 50 in the supporting staff, engaged in the design of equipment for liquefied gas handling. Liquefiers at Tonawanda include a liquid hydrogen plant which can also be used to produce liquid neon.

ARTHUR D. LITTLE, INC.

An organization founded in 1886, Arthur D. Little, Inc. is engaged in contract research for industrial and government clients in a wide variety of fields. Cryogenics became an important area of concentration for this organization in the period 1940 - 1950 when the production of the Collins helium liquefier was begun.

In this same period, much work was also done on mobile liquid oxygen generating and handling equipment for aircraft. Research in this period included studies of superconductivity and development of the concept of the frictionless gyroscope.

From 1951 to 1955, cryogenic work at A. D. Little centered on integrated systems for handling large quantities of such cryogenic fluids as oxygen, hydrogen, deuterium and methane. This included design of road transport vehicles and pumps for these fluids.

In 1956 - 1957, the emphasis shifted to cryogenic propellant loading and handling systems for missiles, and broadened to include work on cryopumping, a technique for high vacuum production by freezing out residual gases, which brought large test environment chambers for space hardware within the realm of economic feasibility. Also during this period, work was carried out in such diverse fields as cryogenic computers and the bulk transport of liquid methane.

Since 1958, work has been concentrated in the hydrogen-helium area, but has covered a wide spectrum of cryogenic hardware items and processes. It has included cryogenic cooling devices for infra-red sensors, cryogenic storage techniques for biological materials and new types of low-temperature insulation.

NBS-AEC CRYOGENIC ENGINEERING LABORATORY

The idea of a separate United States Government cryogenic laboratory originated in 1949 with Dr. Edward F. Hammel, then head of the Cryogenic Laboratory of the Los Alamos Scientific Laboratory. The original impetus was provided by needs of the U. S. Atomic Energy Commission for a facility for the study of low-temperature processes and equipment for gas separation and handling in connection with various nuclear devices, including nuclear rockets.

Ground was broken in May 1951 at Boulder, Colorado and construction was completed in the early spring of 1952 on a site which had recently been acquired by the National Bureau of Standards through the generosity of merchants and citizens of

Boulder, who acquired the 210-acre property and deeded it to the Government.

The goal of the Laboratory is to improve the convenience, safety and efficiency of producing, storing and handling low temperature refrigerants in large quantities. Much of the emphasis has been placed on hydrogen. The cryogenic plant has a capacity of 400-450 liters per hour of liquid nitrogen and 350 liters per hour of liquid hydrogen. This rate of production of liquid hydrogen is greater than that of any other known experimental facility.

MASSACHUSETTS INSTITUTE OF TECHNOLOGY

The appointment in 1949 of Professor Samuel C. Collins as Professor of Cryogenic Engineering in the Department of Mechanical Engineering was the first formal recognition of cryogenic engineering by an appointment on a university faculty.

The first helium liquefier or Collins Cryostat was built in 1946. It had a capacity of four liters of liquid helium per hour. An improved and larger version of this early machine was built later; it has a production rate of 45 liters of liquid helium per hour and now supplies all the liquid helium used for research in other M.I.T. laboratories.

M.I.T. offers a first year graduate course entitled "Advanced Projects in Thermodynamics" given by Professor Collins and others. There is a first or second year graduate course in "Low Temperature Refrigeration" also given by Collins. In the realm of cryogenic applications there is a course in "Food Engineering" in the Department of Mechanical Engineering which deals with fundamental principles of thermodynamics with specific application to problems in heat transfer, refrigeration, and air conditioning as related to food processing and preservation. There is also a refrigerating and air conditioning laboratory course. Of these various courses the most definitely in the cryogenic area is the "Low Temperature Refrigeration."

In addition, the Lincoln Laboratory which is operated by M.I.T., is an electronics research center of major importance.

Here the study of the low-noise characteristics of electronic circuits operated at cryogenic temperatures furnish the incentive for much low-temperature research.

UNIVERSITY OF MICHIGAN

Cryogenic work at the University of Michigan at Ann Arbor, Michigan is divided between the Department of Chemistry and the Department of Mechanical Engineering.

The work in the Department of Chemistry under Professor Edgar F. Westrum has concentrated on thermodynamic properties from the point of view of the physical chemist. Facilities include a precise adiabatic calorimeter which permits maintenance of temperatures from about 0.3 degree Kelvin up to room temperature for determination of various thermal data. These are obtained in studies of phase equilibria in complex systems, the enthalpies of mixing in solid solutions, etc.

In the Department of Mechanical Engineering, six faculty members, led by Professor Gordon J. Van Wylen, the Chairman of the Department, are engaged in low-temperature work. In addition, there are about ten predoctoral students working in the Heat Transfer and Thermodynamics Laboratory. Work has included studies of the pressurized discharge of cryogenic fluids from tanks. An outgrowth of this work was a further study on the influence of varying gravity conditions (from high G values to zero gravity) on heat transfer to or from boiling liquids. Other work has included measurements on liquid-vapor equilibria of various cryogenic fluids.

A graduate-level course in "Refrigeration and Cryogenics" is taught in the Department of Mechanical Engineering. Two weeks are spent on conventional refrigeration and the remainder of the time on cryogenics. The course is given each spring semester to about 12 students. In addition, short courses in "Cryogenic Engineering Fundamentals" have been given to students from industry and from Government laboratories.

UNIVERSITY OF CALIFORNIA

Research in low-temperatures at the University of California at Berkeley has been divided between the Departments of Chemistry and Physics, with relatively less emphasis in the School of Engineering, where courses in air conditioning and refrigeration are offered. For his work in this field, Professor William F. Giauque, Professor Emeritus of Chemistry, received the Nobel Prize in 1949. The concentration of fundamental work in the science departments has been reinforced by the assignment of faculty members from those departments to the staff of the Lawrence Radiation Laboratory, which is operated for the U. S. Atomic Energy Commission by the University of California.

In addition to cryogenic work at the campus at Berkeley, ultrasonic studies at cryogenic temperatures are carried out at the University of California at Los Angeles. Still more cryogenic research is carried out at the campus at Riverside, California.

The University of California also operates the Los Alamos Scientific Laboratory at Los Alamos, New Mexico for the Atomic Energy Commission. As mentioned earlier in the discussion of the AEC-NBS Cryogenic Engineering Laboratory, much important cryogenic work has originated at Los Alamos; the work of that Laboratory today includes a broad range study of the physical properties of the various forms of helium.

CENTERS OF SPECIALIZED ELECTRONIC AND MAGNETIC WORK

There are a number of industrial research centers which devote part of their efforts to cryogenic research. In the latest (1960) census of industrial research laboratories by the National Research Council of the National Academy of Sciences, some 28 laboratories list cryogenics a specific area of interest. There are certainly hundreds of laboratories using cryogenic methods, even though they may not regard cryogenics, *per se,* as a major area of research concentration.

One major industrial area of applied cryogenics is that of masers, lasers and other electronic devices which operate at low temperatures. Companies working in this field include:

— Bell Telephone Laboratories at Murray Hill, N. J.
— Hughes Research Laboratories at Malibu Beach, California
— Raytheon Company at Lexington, Mass.
— Bendix Systems Division at Ann Arbor, Michigan

Another important industrial cryogenic area is that of superconductive magnets. Included among the companies working in this field are:

— Westinghouse Electric and Manufacturing Co. at Pittsburgh, Pa.
— General Electric Co. — General Engineering Laboratories at Schenectady, N. Y.
— Bell Telephone Laboratories at Murray Hill, N. J.
— Atomics International at Los Angeles, California

Other industrial laboratories are interested primarily in superconducting switches and new compact super-speed computers which function at cryogenic temperatures. These include:

— International Business Machines (IBM) at Poughkeepsie, N. Y.
— General Electric Research Laboratory at Schenectady, N. Y.

Chapter 5

HOW COLD IS MEASURED

The measurement of temperature may be based upon many different heat effects. The thermal expansion in volume of a body of mercury suffices for the temperature range covered by everyday thermometers, but mercury freezes and becomes useless as a thermometer fluid at —39°C. Toluene and pentane can be employed as thermometer fluids down to the temperatures of solid carbon dioxide and liquid air, respectively. At liquid air temperatures and certainly at lower temperatures, fluid expansion must be replaced by the expansion of gases or vapors, or by changes in electrical, magnetic or other properties of substances. However, before discussing temperature measurement in detail, a discussion of temperature scales is clearly in order.

TEMPERATURE SCALES

Temperature scales are usually defined in terms of one or two arbitrarily chosen points. The most commonly used scale in the United States and Great Britain is the Fahrenheit scale which was invented by the German scientist Fahrenheit in the eighteenth century. His scale has two fixed points, the freezing point of water at 32°F., and its boiling point at 212°F. A mercury thermometer is the standard (although other fluids may replace it) and the scale between the two fixed points is divided uniformly into 180 degrees.* The Fahrenheit thermometer is used in engineering practice and in medicine, and suffices for temperatures in the range encountered in everyday life.

The European counterpart of the Fahrenheit scale is the centigrade scale, which is used in science the world over. It was invented by the Swedish astronomer, Anders Celsius, in 1742. When it was developed, the boiling point of water was designated as the zero point and the freezing point of water as the 100-degree point, giving an inverted temperature scale. Later it was put right side up and became the common centigrade or Celsius scale. This scale also suffices to measure all everyday temperatures.

Other scales have been developed but discarded. One was the Réaumur scale which was invented by Rene Antoine Ferchault de Réaumur about 1730. Its zero point was the freezing point of water and its upper limit was the boiling point of alcohol (approximately 80°C).

The definition of a more fundamental temperature scale, whose zero point is the ultimate lower limit of temperature, was the work of Lord Kelvin. In 1848, he proposed the scale which is that of absolute centigrade temperature. On it absolute zero is 0° Kelvin and the freezing point of water is 273.18° Kelvin. (See Figure 5-1.)

The counterpart of the Kelvin scale for the American or British engineer is the Rankine scale or absolute Fahrenheit scale which was developed by the Scottish engineer, William John Macquorn Rankine. On this scale, absolute zero is 0° Rankine, and the freezing point of water is 491.69° Rankine.

THERMOMETERS

The choice of a thermometer for a particular purpose depends upon a number of considerations. First of all is the temperature range to be measured which, as has already been stated, may limit the number of types from which a selection can be made.

---

* The zero point Fahrenheit used was the temperature of a freezing mixture of ice and salt, and his second point is believed to have been a rough value of 100°F. for the normal human body temperature.

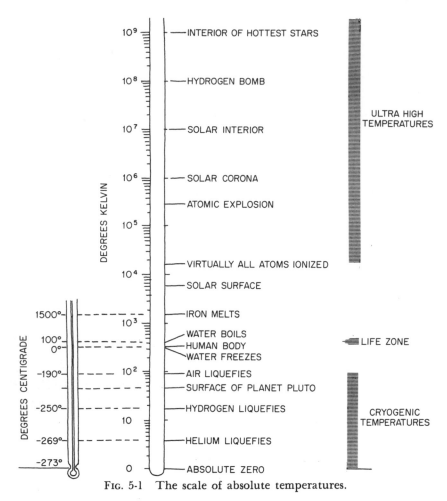

FIG. 5-1   The scale of absolute temperatures.

Then there are the important criteria of sensitivity, accuracy and reproductibility, that is, how small a temperature difference can be detected, within what limits of instrumental error is the measurement true, and how do those limits vary from time to time. Another consideration that is particularly important in doing research on small quantities of material, and is often the case at liquid helium temperatures, is the effect of the temperature measurement upon the material or system being measured. Obviously this effect should be a minimum. Two other considerations entering into the choice of a thermometer are the obvious ones of cost and simplicity of construction and operation.

Gas Thermometers

A type of thermometer that is very useful in low-temperature works is the constant-volume gas thermometer. This instrument measures the changes in pressure due to changes in temperature of a body of gas held at constant volume. A representative constant-volume gas thermometer is shown in Figure 5-2. A dewar (shown by the broken line) incloses the thermometer bulb, which is connected by a small-bore tube to a manometer filled with mercury. As the temperature in the dewar changes, the volume of gas in the bulb (which is large compared to the gas volume in the capillary) changes also, but the adjustable mercury reservoir is moved to keep the volume constant at the index point. Since

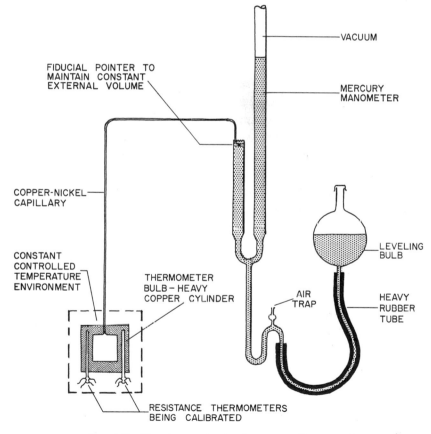

FIG. 5-2 Simple constant-volume gas thermometer.

the volume of mercury in the left leg of the manometer is constant, the movement of the reservoir causes a change in the mercury level in the right leg of the manometer; this change corresponds to the pressure change within the bulb due to temperature change.

Although a gas thermometer of this type is not simple, it can be used, in skilled hands, to measure very low temperatures quite accurately. A simpler but less accurate gas thermometer would indicate the pressure more directly by a connection of the capillary to a bourdon-tube type of pressure gage.

While gas pressure thermometry can give very precise measurements, it is beset by many sources of error for which corrections must be made if such precision is to be attained. The capillary contains gas at a temperature other than that being measured. The volume of the thermometer itself changes with temperature. The pressure-temperature function of the gas must be used in calculations, since the error introduced by assuming ideal gas behavior is too great for accurate work.

Vapor Pressure Thermometers

Using vapor pressure to measure temperature affords an index of high accuracy but of limited scope, since the temperature range over which any given substance exerts a measurable vapor pressure is relatively small. If one regards vapor pressures from 50 mm of mercury to 1000 mm of mercury as a useful range, one can use various liquids as follows:

Fluid	Range, °K		
Helium	2.3	to	4.5
Hydrogen	13.8	to	21.2
Neon	21	to	28
Nitrogen	63	to	80
Oxygen	74	to	93
Methane	92	to	116
Nitric oxide	107	to	123
Carbon tetrafluoride	121	to	145
Ethylene	141	to	184

A mercury manometer can be used to measure the vapor pressure in the same manner that it is used to measure gas pressure as shown in Figure 5-2. Purity of the material whose vapor pressure is being measured is perhaps the most critical consideration in the construction of this type of thermometer.

Resistance Thermometers

A thermometer employing the measurement of variation of the electrical resistance of platinum metal with temperature is as useful as the gas thermometer in cryogenic work. Its readings are quite reproducible and it is more sensitive than the gas thermometer. The platinum resistance thermometer is useful over a wide temperature range, and is simple to manufacture and use. The resistance of the platinum helix generally used as the measuring element is measured either by a Wheatstone bridge or one of its many modifications, or by a potentiometer, which is connected to compare the potential drop across the thermometer with the drop across a standard resistance carrying the same current.

The platinum resistance thermometer may be used down as low as 14°K, the freezing point of hydrogen. Copper wire can be used in resistance thermometry down to 20°K and lead wire to 9°K. Recently pure indium metal has been used down to the point where it becomes superconductive (and essentially loses all resistance) at 3.4°K. Indium thus gives the experimenter a long-desired instrument, a single thermometer which is useful from room temperature down into the liquid helium range.

Semiconducting Resistance Thermometers

The word "Thermistor" is a trade name for a semiconductor thermometer. Its resistance varies exponentially with temperature and it has a negative temperature coefficient; thus lower temperatures give higher resistances plus greater sensitivity. The increase in resistance with decrease in temperature is the converse of the behavior of metals. Unfortunately, the resistance of "Thermistors" increases so rapidly as the temperature decreases that it may limit the range of temperatures which can be measured with these devices. There is also the practical problem of making good electrical contacts with semiconductor materials.

Carbon was first used by Giauque in 1936 in the first application of "Thermistor" devices to cryogenic temperature measurement. At the present time, major interest for this use is being directed to doped germanium.

Thermocouples

Thermocouples, devices in which a pair of dissimilar metals generates a voltage at a junction, are generally less accurate temperature measuring devices than are resistance thermometers. Thermocouples may be easier to build and to read, but they have the disadvantage of becoming less sensitive at lower temperatures.

Low temperature work with thermocouples can be facilitated by maintaining the reference junction (cold junction), at low temperatures such as that of liquid nitrogen. Thus the voltage to be measured is reduced and any change is proportionately greater in magnitude and easier to measure accurately.

Copper-constantan thermocouples have been used successfully by Giauque and his co-workers at the University of California at Berkeley at temperatures down to 12°K. For use at lower temperatures, more exotic couples have been studied and work at the Kamerlingh Onnes Laboratory at Leiden has produced a gold-cobalt alloy which is joined as one element of a couple with a silver-gold alloy as the other.

MEASURING QUANTITIES OF COLD FLUIDS

The measurement of cold fluids is made more complicated than the measurement of flow or liquid level at room temperature by two main factors:

— the tendency of the cryogenic fluids to boil at low temperatures giving a two-phase mixture whose properties are not those of the fluid presumably being measured.

— the tendency of the cold from the body of fluid being measured to creep to the sensing element, rendering it sluggish or inoperable.

Flow Rate

Calibrated valves afford one simple but approximate method of regulation of the flow of cryogenic liquids. However, measurement of flow in a pipeline in a reasonably precise manner requires metering.

Displacement meters have been used successfully in measuring cryogenic liquid flow, for example, that of liquid oxygen. Such a meter employs intermeshing rotors. Liquid flow causes them to rotate and the motion is transmitted through gears to a counter, which is thermally separated from the meter body and which operates at ambient temperature. For liquid oxygen, hard graphitic carbon rotors have performed successfully. For liquid nitrogen service, wax-impregnated rotors have been found satisfactory.

Oscillating-piston meters of the positive displacement type have also been used commercially. One type has an aluminum piston in a bronze meter casing.

Turbine-type flowmeters, which are also of the positive displacement type, have been used successfully in cryogenic service. These are packless meters containing a bar magnet within the rotor. Magnet rotation is sensed from the outside by a coil and the resultant induced voltage is measured.

Orifice meters have been used, but have not been outstandingly successful, due to vaporization of the cryogenic fluid at the orifice entrance and in the pressure tap connections.

Liquid Level

Levels of cryogenic liquids in vessels may be determined in a number of ways, Among the simplest techniques are the placement of the vessel on a scale for indirect measurement or the use of a slit-silvered Dewar vessel for direct viewing of liquid level.

Liquid level measuring instruments which are mounted in the vessel and which contact the liquid are represented by a wide variety of specific devices. Perhaps the simplest is a float with a long stem and an indicator protruding from the top of the vessel;

however, such a device may allow excessive leakage of heat and materials.

A simple hydrostatic gage may be used to indicate level in terms of pressure differential between the top and bottom of a tank. Oscillations may plague such systems, however, and gages employing resistance measurements using platinum resistors or semiconductor resistors have found wider application. Such a device is shown in Figure 5-3. Capacitance measurements may also be used to measure liquid levels effectively.

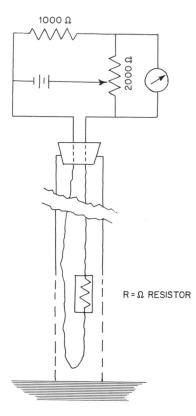

FIG. 5-3   A carbon resistor used as
liquid helium level finder.

Ultrasonic gaging devices have been applied to liquid level measurements in cryogenic systems as shown in Figure 5-4. The use of a "still well" to reduce thermal turbulence may be desirable. A transformer-type liquid level sensor is shown in Figure 5-5.

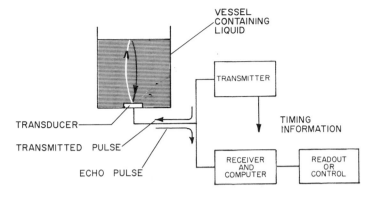

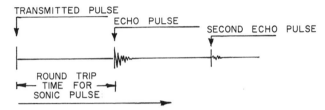

FIG. 5-4 Ultrasonic measurement of cryogenic liquid level.

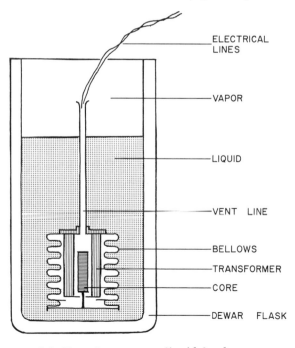

FIG. 5-5 Transformer type liquid level sensor.

Chapter 6

HOW COLD AFFECTS THE
PROPERTIES OF MATERIALS

As soon as liquid air, liquid hydrogen, and liquid helium became available around the turn of the century, attention was focused on the effects that the temperatures produced by these newly-available fluids might have on the properties of materials.

The usual experiments to show the properties of liquid air include the freezing of a hollow rubber ball which then is smashed to bits when one attempts to bounce it, the manufacture of a mercury "hammer" by pouring liquid air over a small quantity of mercury in a wooden mold, the manufacture of a spring from a piece of lead wire, and the fashioning of a bell with clear tones from a bell-shaped piece of lead which, of course, previously emitted only dull sounds at room temperature. Such experiments are striking and demonstrative but not very scientific.

Along more scientific and practical lines, Hadfield and Dewar in 1900 made the first studies on the tensile properties of some irons and steels at liquid air temperatures. Hadfield and de Haas extended these investigations to liquid hydrogen temperatures in 1933.

Now that we are working with greater quantities of cryogenic fluids, transporting them over greater distances, and making them perform in more complex types of apparatus, our knowledge of the effects of low temperatures on materials must be more and more sophisticated. The very life of man in space, for example, depends on such knowledge.

STRENGTH OF MATERIALS

Determination of the strength of materials at cryogenic temperatures is vitally important to permit the efficient and safe design of cryogenic equipment, since low temperatures have marked effects on the physical properties of many materials, in many cases inducing a disastrous degree of brittleness.

Figure 6-1 shows an apparatus for the determination of the tensile strength of metals at very low temperatures. Figure 6-2 shows some of the results obtained in such an apparatus and illustrates the effect of temperature on yield strength. In general, the metals which have a body-centered cubic lattice show a pronounced increase in yield strength (and a corresponding loss of ductility) with decreasing temperature; such metals, including iron and tungsten and molybdenum, are thus unsuitable for the construction of low-temperature apparatus. On the other hand, metals which have a face-centered cubic lattice show only a slight increase in yield strength and retain their room-temperature ductility at temperatures as low as 77°K. The metals in this latter category which are suitable materials of construction for low-temperature apparatus include copper, nickel, and aluminum.

However, ductility alone is not an adequate guide to the suitability of materials; impact strength must also be considered. Thus, some carbon steels have been found to show elongations of as much as 15 per cent in tensile tests at —160°C (—256°F), yet were glass-brittle in impact tests. Conversely, some high-strength stainless steels with elongation values of only about 2 per cent have shown excellent toughness in impact tests.

Copper alloys, aluminum alloys, and stainless steel, as well as titanium alloys, are most commonly used in the fabrication of cryogenic storage vessels and transfer equipment.

It is also interesting to observe the effects of very low temperatures on the strength of other materials. Figure 6-3 shows some of the results of tests on a number of plastics. Only Teflon, of

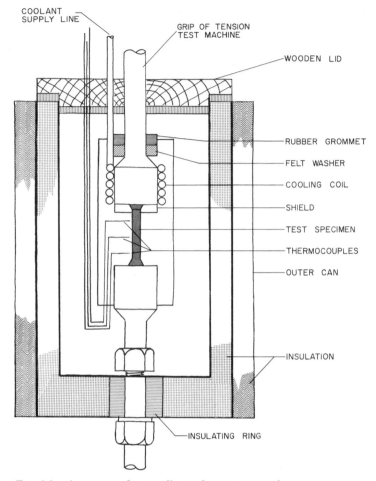

FIG. 6-1 Apparatus for tensile testing at cryogenic temperatures.

the plastics tested, showed ductility down to the lowest test temperature, which was 4° Kelvin. However, Mylar films of 1 mil thickness or less showed good flexibility in bending tests at temperatures as low as 20°K. Glass fiber laminates also stood up well in performance tests. However, it is obvious that much more remains to be learned about the behavior of plastics, particularly in various physical forms, at very low temperatures.

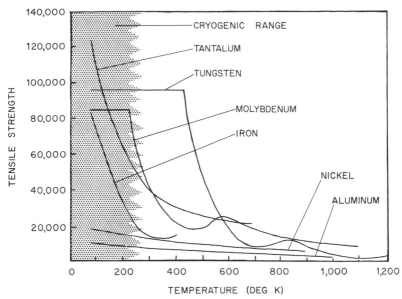

FIG. 6-2   Effect of cryogenic temperatures of tensile properties of metals.

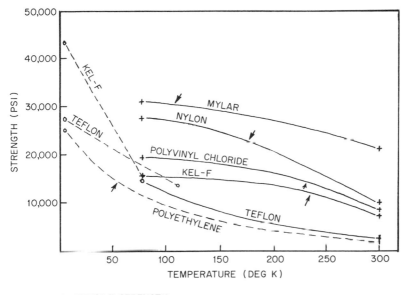

+ = TENSILE STRENGTH
O = COMPRESSIVE YIELD STRENGTH
ARROWS INDICATE APPROXIMATE BOUNDRIES
BETWEEN BRITTLE AND DUCTILE FAILURE

FIG. 6-3   Temperature vs. strength for various plastics.

FRICTION AND WEAR PROPERTIES

Friction and wear properties of materials at cryogenic temperatures are critical in the design of pumps for cryogenic fluids. There is no particular reason to assume that most cryogenic fluids are other than poor lubricants; surprisingly enough, however, conventional bearing and seal designs have been operated in liquid nitrogen and hydrogen without difficulty. This is particularly surprising in the light of the fact that oxide films often prevent surface welding during sliding contact; nitrogen and hydrogen tend to prevent re-formation or repair of such oxide films once they are broken or disrupted.

However, in an attempt to insure that welding of contact surfaces can not occur, much development work has been done on combinations of metals and non-metals. Carbon-filled Teflon as a slider on a sliding or bearing surface in contact with steel has shown considerable promise. A carbon surface riding on a Teflon-filled porous bronze also gave good friction and wear characteristics.

In general, frictional characteristics in liquid nitrogen were similar to those measured at room temperature; but wear was in general lesser in amount at liquid nitrogen temperatures.

ADHESIVE PROPERTIES

The strength of structural adhesives at cryogenic temperatures is an important consideration because adhesive-bonded metallic sandwich construction and adhesive-bonded honeycomb construction is being used so widely. In tests on aluminum bonded to aluminum and on stainless steel bonded to stainless steel, it has been found that phenolic adhesives (vinyl-phenolic and rubber-phenolic) tend to decrease greatly in ultimate strength at low temperatures, whereas epoxy-type adhesives tend to maintain their strength over a wide temperature range. This is true of both epoxy-phenolic and filled epoxide combinations, as shown in Figure 6-4. In fact, the best low-temperature adhesives have

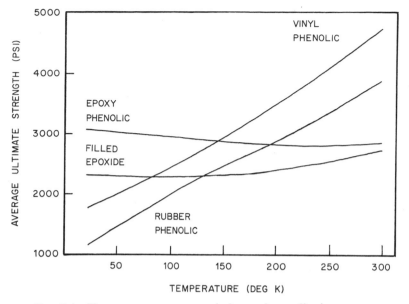

FIG. 6-4 Temperature vs. strength for various adhesive systems.

been found to be epoxy or epoxy-phenolic resins supported on glass cloth and filled with sufficient metallic powder to approach the coefficient of thermal expansion of the adherend.

THERMAL PROPERTIES

In the design of cryogenic apparatus, there are three principal types of solids whose thermal conductivity values are important, pure metals, alloys and dielectrics. Some typical values are shown in Figure 6-5. It will be noted that conductivity maxima are sometimes encountered at 20 to 50°K. In this range, pure metals have conductivities 100 times as large as their alloys. The alloys themselves differ from one another by a factor of ten. Dielectrics having a disordered structure, such as glass and plastics, have very low thermal conductivities; in contrast, the crystal dielectrics like diamond and sapphire have very high conductivities. It should be noted that the temperature variations as well as the absolute values of conductivity of these three types of materials have a wide range.

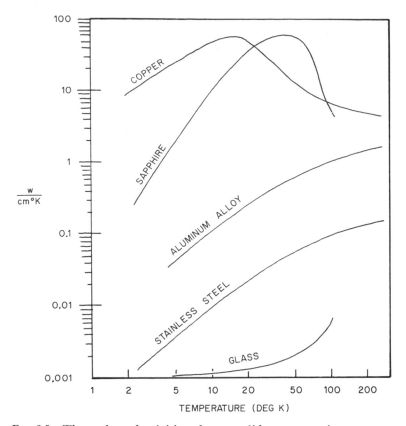

Fɪɢ. 6-5   Thermal conductivities of some solids at cryogenic temperatures.

The specific heat, the amount of heat needed to raise a unit quantity of material one degree in temperature, increases as temperature increases. Conversely, at very low temperatures, only very small quantities of heat are required to change the temperature of a body. Thus 6000 times as much heat must be applied to raise the temperature of a piece of copper from 300° Kelvin to 301° Kelvin as is required to raise the temperature of the same piece of copper from 2° Kelvin to 3° Kelvin.

ELECTRICITY CONDUCTIVITY

As one lowers the temperature of any metal, the electrical resistivity decreases. Thus, at cryogenic temperatures, the resistivity of copper drops to value so low that a Number 40 wire carries a current of 4 amperes without damage; this is twice the fusing current of such a wire at room temperature.

Alloys usually have electrical resistivities higher than those of the constituent elements at room temperature. This effect is accentuated at cryogenic temperatures because the drop in resistance of alloys with decrease in temperature is low compared to the corresponding change for pure metals. Thus constantan (60 parts copper and 40 nickel) has a resistance at cryogenic temperatures 95% of that at room temperature, in marked contrast with the very small resistances of pure metals at cryogenic temperatures.

Electrical insulators usually become even more effective at cryogenic temperatures; this may be due to the fact that surface moisture films become less conductive. Most cryogenic fluids are good electrical insulators. Examples are helium, hydrogen and nitrogen.

Semiconductor materials such as silicon and germanium offer an interesting combination of properties at cryogenic temperatures. They have high thermal conductivity while their electrical conductivity is as low as that of most insulating materials.

SUPERCONDUCTIVITY

The electrical resistivity of some metals seems to vanish altogether at temperatures a few degrees above absolute zero. The atoms in the solid may still be vibrating, but they no longer interefere with electron flow through it.

Superconductivity was discovered by Heike Kamerlingh Onnes in the course of an experiment in which he passed an electric current through frozen mercury. Since that time, workers at many laboratories have extended our insight into the theory of this phenomenon and have also found a host of potential applications. One laboratory particularly noteworthy in both of these areas is the Bell Telephone Laboratories at Murray Hill, New Jersey. They have, for instance, determined which of the elements in the periodic table exhibit the phenomenon of superconductivity.

The fact that the resistance drops to zero in the superconductive state has been demonstrated dramatically by Professor S. C. Collins of M.I.T.; he induced a current in a superconducting ring of metallic lead in March 1954. In September 1956 he measured the current and found it to be identical to the current put in two and one half years before, within one part in 10^{11}.

The frictionless flow of electricity through solids known as superconductivity still does not have a precise scientific explanation. A recent theory postulates that normal electrical resistance is produced when the flowing electrons which constitute an electric current are knocked out of their paths by collision with heavy metallic atoms; in superconductors the electrons manage to get past the atoms without being deflected. The theory goes on to suggest that they are able to do so because, instead of moving as individuals, electrons move in pairs. It is as if they are dancing through the metal in couples instead of drifting along as individuals. In a superconducting metal, the vibrations of the metallic atoms are slowed down to the point where they are unable to break the pairs. Thus the flow of the current becomes frictionless.

This phenomenon can be of immense practical importance in the operation of high field electromagnets for high-energy accelerators or for fusion power devices. The electromagnets would require only an initial power input to start the current in their coils, plus a modest power input required for refrigeration, instead of a very great power input required to maintain the current in the coils of such huge magnets at room temperatures.

Superconductivity is also applied in the operation of cryogenic memory devices for computers which permit "shrinking" a roomful of conventional memory elements to a suitcase-sized memory operated at liquid helium temperatures.

Entire books have been written on the subject of superconductivity. It is our purpose here simply to mention a few of the

fundamentals and to concentrate on the applications. One fundamental observation is that electrical resistivity of all metals
decreases with temperature, and that of some metals drops
sharply to near zero at a temperature near absolute zero (See
Figure 6-6). Thus, the first fundamental is that the temperature

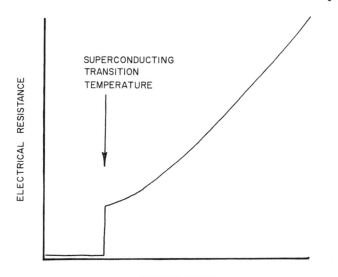

FIG. 6-6 Conductivity of a potential superconductor
at cryogenic temperatures.

must be very low. Indeed, technetium at 11°K has the highest
transition temperature observed for any pure element, although
alloys remain superconductive at somewhat higher temperatures.
A niobium-tin alloy, for example, remains superconductive at
18°K.

A second fundamental observation is the behavior of semi-
conductors with respect to magnetic fields. They tend to expel
magnetic fields below a certain magnetic field strength, but the
superconductivity disappears in magnetic fields exceeding that
critical value. This fundamental observation has been found
not to apply to all materials, however, and high field strength
cryogenic magnets can now be made. This breakthrough resulted
from studies at Bell Telephone Laboratories on the size of the
critical field which quenches superconductivity in a material

as a function of the composition of the material. For the classical superconductors, mercury, tin, and lead, this field is about 400 gauss. Work by Bell scientists revealed that a niobium-tin alloy could resist 50,000 gauss. The upper limit of tolerance for vanadium-gallium has been predicted at 800,000 gauss.

SUPERFLUIDITY

Superfluidity is a phenomenon which occurs only in liquid helium, and what is more, only in liquid helium which is cooled below 2.2°K, which is two degrees below the boiling point of helium. At this very low temperature, helium becomes a super-fluid. One of the astonishing properties of this superfluid is that it flows uphill! As shown in Figure 6-7, a test tube of superfluid

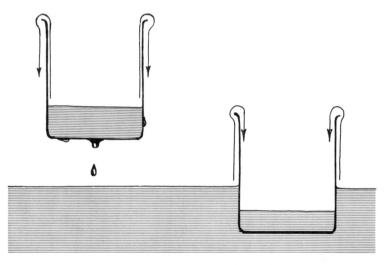

FIG. 6-7   How superfluidity looks.

helium held over a larger bath will empty itself as the super-fluid climbs out of its container.

The phenomenon is called superfluidity because the superfluid is capable of flowing through narrow capillaries and channels that are impervious to most gases, and certainly to all liquids. The viscosity of superfluid helium, which is called helium II (in contrast to ordinary liquid helium which exists in the range 2.2 to 4.2°K and is called helium I), is less than 1/1000 of a micropoise, which is smaller than the viscosity of any gas by a factor of ten.

Superfluid helium or helium II is the best conductor of heat known; it is 190 times more conductive than copper. In fact, it transmits heat almost a tenth as rapidly as the air around us transmits sound; for this and other reasons heat conduction in superfluid helium is sometimes referred to as "second sound."

Chapter 7

HOW COLD IS CONTAINED

As we have seen, a fair bit of skill is required to obtain cryogenic fluids at liquid air temperatures of 80 - 90°K and a good deal more to get down to the hydrogen-neon range of 20°K. Real ingenuity is required to take the third step to attain liquid helium temperatures of 4°K.

Fully as much care in design is required to store these fluids at room temperature without excessively rapid evaporation, which arises from two circumstances. In the first place, heat flow from the surroundings at room temperature (293°K) to the various cold fluids is relatively easy because of the driving force for heat transfer due to the great temperature difference. This can be counteracted only by very effective insulation. In the second place, such heat as does leak causes a large loss, due to the low latent heats of the cryogenic fluids. While hydrogen has a latent heat of 107 cal/gm, nitrogen and oxygen have latent heats of only 50 cal/gm. Neon has an even lower latent heat value, about 20 cal/gm, while helium is at the extreme with a latent heat of only 5 cal/gm.

One very useful and practical measurement of insulation effectiveness is the rate of boil-off of a particular cryogenic fluid in a vessel of given size with a given type of insulation.

Taking helium first as the most difficult fluid to contain, we find that conventional transportable helium cryostats can be designed with a boil-off of 1% per day. In contrast, a large liquid hydrogen tank might have a boil-off of 10% per year.

74

INSULATION

Since the boiling points of the fluids are fixed, as are their low latent heats of vaporization, the only means of realizing reasonably loss-free storage of these cryogenic fluids is to provide very efficient insulation.

Vacuum-Walled Containers

Double-walled vessels with a high vacuum between the walls and with highly reflective surfaces facing the vacuum space are the "Dewar vessels" or simply "dewars" invented by James Dewar.

One type is a glass vessel having the outer wall of the fluid container and the inner wall of the outer container silvered (See Figure 3-2). Another type is a doube-walled copper vessel with the corresponding surfaces scrupulously cleaned to achieve the high intrinsic reflectivity of copper. A body of charcoal adsorbent may be affixed to the outer wall of the fluid container, where it is kept cold and helps to condense any gases remaining in the vacuum space after it is evacuated and sealed off (See Figure 8-10).

Plastic Foams

Foamed plastic materials containing many small cells which are not connected are good cryogenic insulating materials. Polystyrene is the plastic which has met with the greatest success in this type of application. Foamed nitrile rubbers have also proved satisfactory. Polyurethane foams have been studied for this use, but tend to break up due to thermal expansion and contraction; they also tend to age and to lose the fluorinated hydrocarbon gases with which they are blown. However plastic foams are perhaps only 1/5 as effective as a good dewar from a a heat transfer standpoint, chiefly because plastic foams do have solid conducting paths which are continuous, even though they may be tortuous. Thus the efficiency of these foams does not approach that of a vacuum, or even more, of a powdered material in a vacuum.

One interesting possibility is that of making vessels for cryo-genic liquids entirely from these foamed plastics. Vessels may be fabricated to handle liquid nitrogen or liquid hydrogen by cutting foamed polystyrene to shape and cementing it, where necessary, with epoxy cement.

Powder-vacuum

In a dewar vessel, heat transfer is almost entirely by radiation. The substitution of evacuated powders for high vacuum alone will usually improve the insulation by reducing the radiant heat transfer. In the case of liquid nitrogen or hydrogen, the effectiveness of insulation may be improved by a factor of 6 or 7.

In powder-vacuum insulation, the insulating vacuum space is filled with a fine light powder such as perlite, silica aerogel, carbon black or diatomaceous earth. When powders are used, the vacuum requirements are made less extreme (that is, the space need not be so highly evacuated); minimum heat transfer is closely approached at 10 microns of mercury pressure in a space filled with perlite or silica aerogel. In order for vacuum-powder insulation to be used effectively, however, the temperature difference between the walls should be appreciable (one wall at room temperature) and the insulating space should be at least 10 centimeters (4 inches) thick.

The thermal conductivity of the powder may be decreased and the powder may be made more opaque to infra-red radiation by admixture with finely-divided copper or aluminum. About 50% copper and 50% light powder is the combination most often used; the thermal conductivity of such a mixture is only about 1/5 as great as that of a straight light powder-vacuum combination.

Insulating powders do pose some unique operating and main-tenance problems. Since they flow like liquids, they will fill in well around piping or intricate structural shapes. In case access is required to some part enclosed in the powder, a portion can not be removed for inspection (as in the case of a conventional insulating material); the powder in the jacket must be blown to a storage silo and returned when the work is completed.

Figure 7-1 shows a powder-vacuum insulated tank in cross

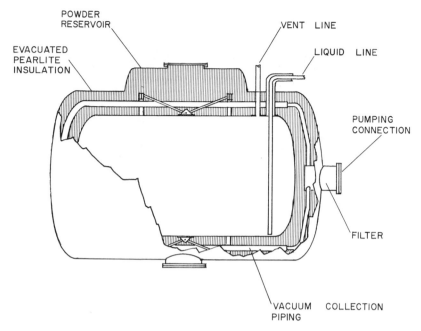

FIG. 7-1 A powder-vacuum insulated tank in cross section.

section. The vessel shown is a liquid hydrogen dewar suitable for mounting on a truck trailer. It is to be noted that there is a powder reservoir at the top of the tank to insure that the double-walled vacuum space is kept full of powder.

Superinsulation

The need for better insulation, particularly in the hydrogen-helium range, led to the search for a new type of insulation which might be an order of magnitude better than metal-plus-light-powder-vacuum insulation. The search turned to that of finding some means of providing radiation-reflective shields separated from the vessel surfaces and from one another by low-conductivity fillers.

Alternate layers of aluminum foil and glass fiber mats in "club sandwich" fashion, having as many as 80 layers per inch, provided an acceptable solution to the problem, and such insulation is now incorporated into commercial storage and transport containers

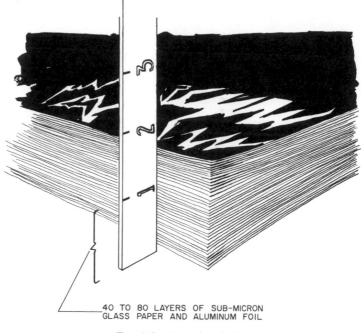

40 TO 80 LAYERS OF SUB-MICRON
GLASS PAPER AND ALUMINUM FOIL

Fig. 7-2   Superinsulation.

under the trade-marked name of Superinsulation. Figure 7-2
shows the construction of the material and Figure 7-3 illustrates
its application to a hydrogen transport container. It should be
noted that the vacuum required in the jacket for effective
utilization of these Superinsulations must be about 10 times
better, 1 micron rather than 10 microns, than that required for
powder-vacuum insulation.

Another possible construction for superefficient low-temperature insulation involves the use of aluminized Mylar (polyethyl-
ene terephthalate) film. Multilayers are formed of 0.25 mil Mylar
having an aluminum coating 0.001 mil thick and crinkled to
minimize interlayer contact.

One of the interesting features of Superinsulation is that it is
also well adapted to high temperature work; in fact it can be
used over the entire range from absolute zero to $+2200°F$.

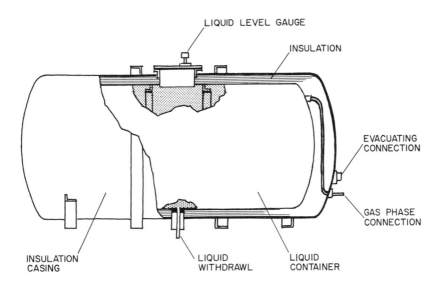

FIG. 7-3   Liquid hydrogen transport container insulated with superinsulation.

THE HYDROGEN PROBLEM

Liquid hydrogen poses a unique problem in storage and handling. The general problems of large temperature difference from the surroundings and of fairly low latent heat of vaporization have been discussed already. In addition to these, liquid hydrogen presents another problem. It exists in two forms, ortho and para, and in changing from ortho to para gives off an appreciable amount of heat at liquid hydrogen temperatures, just where heat is not wanted.

Ordinary hydrogen is the simplest of atoms, consisting of a proton in the center and one electron moving around it, both of which are spinning on their axes. When the electron spins in a pair of such atoms are opposite, they are free to join a molecule of H_2. Then depending on whether the two protons are spinning in the same direction (ortho) or in opposite directions (para) we may have two kinds of hydrogen (See Figure 7-4).

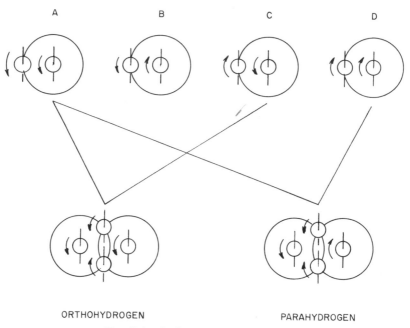

HYDROGEN ATOMS

ORTHOHYDROGEN   PARAHYDROGEN

Fig. 7-4   Ortho and para hydrogen.

At room temperature, the ortho form is present in a ratio of 3 to 1 to the para form. However, at liquid hydrogen temperatures, most of the hydrogen is in the para form. Thus liquefaction of warm hydrogen gives a liquid high in the ortho form, much of which will change to the para form, evolving heat as it does so. The problem is to hasten this conversion at the point where liquid hydrogen is being manufactured so that liquid hydrogen is not shipped in an ortho to para ratio above the equilibrium value, which would be a built-in heat source, making low-loss shipment and storage impossible. It was found at Los Alamos Scientific Laboratory several years ago that metallic oxide catalysts, such as chromic oxide, can hasten this conversion, giving a storable para hydrogen product. Later work at the NBS Cryogenic Engineering Laboratory at Boulder, Colorado showed that iron oxide was even more effective. The flow scheme used in this conversion is shown in Figure 7-5.

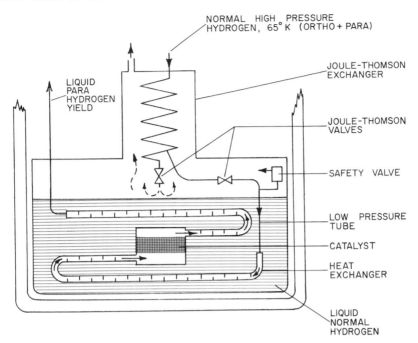

FIG. 7-5 Ortho-para conversion in liquid hydrogen production.

Chapter 8

HOW COLD IS TRANSPORTED

Cryogenic gases may be transported in general in one of two ways: by batch lots in special containers such as dewars, or by flow through specially insulated pipe transfer systems. Each scheme has its advantages and disadvantages. Transport containers are expensive but they can be moved over very long distances. Transfer systems are relatively inexpensive and can transport cryogenic liquids at high rates but only over limited distances. Figure 8-1 shows a typical industrial distribution scheme for liquefied gases.

PUMPS

Both reciprocating and rotary pumps have been successfully to handle cryogenic fluids. Reciprocating pumps have been used as adjuncts to air separation columns in handling the high density liquid nitrogen or oxygen. Here they can be used to force the liquid through a heat exchanger where it is vaporized, still at high pressure, and delivered to high-pressure gas cylinders. Reciprocating pumps are also used on trucks in a similar operation where high pressure gas delivery is desired, for cylinder filling or for some process application such as in oil-well servicing.

High volume centrifugal pumps were used for liquid oxygen by the Germans in World War II. The propulsion system of the V-2 rocket incorporated a centrifugal pump which delivered

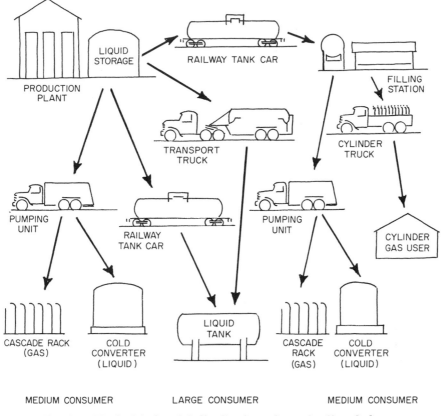

LIQUID
STORAGE

RAILWAY TANK CAR

FILLING
STATION

PRODUCTION
PLANT

TRANSPORT
TRUCK

CYLINDER
TRUCK

PUMPING
UNIT

RAILWAY
TANK CAR

PUMPING
UNIT

CYLINDER
GAS USER

LIQUID
TANK

CASCADE RACK
(GAS)

COLD
CONVERTER
(LIQUID)

CASCADE
RACK
(GAS)

COLD
CONVERTER
(LIQUID)

MEDIUM CONSUMER   LARGE CONSUMER   MEDIUM CONSUMER

FIG. 8-1 Typical industrial distribution scheme for liquefied gases.

150 pounds of liquid oxygen per second, at a delivery pressure
of 300 psi, to burner nozzles in the head of the rocket motor.

A variety of single and multiple stage rotary pumps have now
been applied to cryogenic liquid service. A typical installation
arrangement is shown in Figure 8-2. Questions of bearing design
are the chief problems facing the engineer in the use of such
pumps. They can be avoided by using submerged pumps in
which the packing gland and most or all of the bearing surfaces
are not in contact with the cryogenic fluid.

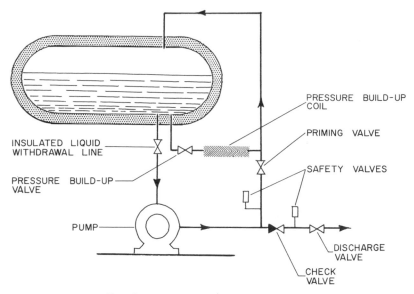

FIG. 8-2 Pump for cryogenic liquid.

HEAT EXCHANGERS

The counterflow heat exchanger has always been one of the most important pieces of cryogenic equipment because it has permitted the continuous liquefaction of the "permanent" gases. It operates by exchanging heat between the outgoing cold fluid and the incoming warm fluid.

The design of such exchangers for maximum efficiency requires large heat transfer surface along with low pressure drop, two requirements which are to some extent in conflict. Figure 8-3 shows a number of the configurations which have been used in an attempt to meet these criteria.

Another possibility is the use of a regenerator or cold accumulator rather than a tubular heat exchanger. This device is similar to the stoves filled with brick checkerwork which are used to recover heat from blast furnace gases. The application of regenerators to the conservation of cold in gas liquefaction plants was pioneered by Frankl in Germany in 1928. A typical flow scheme is shown in Figure 8-4.

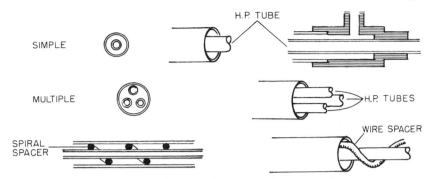

FIG. 8-3   Types of cryogenic heat exchanger surfaces.

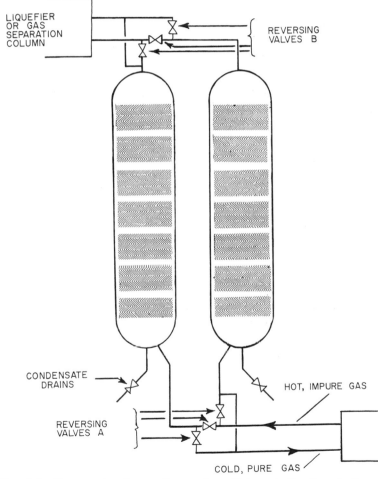

FIG. 8-4   Regenerator for cooling and purifying air for liquefaction.

PIPELINES

While the transfer of small amounts of cryogenic fluids through short, uninsulated tubes in the laboratory involves little difficulty, the problems multiply when large quantities are to be delivered

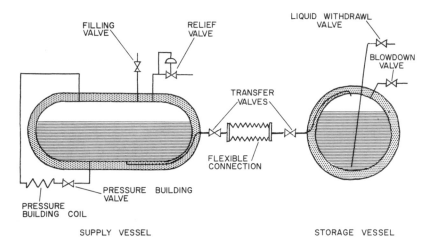

FIG. 8-5   Liquefied gas transfer system.

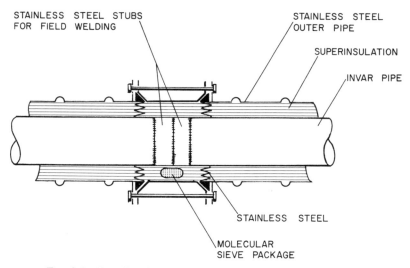

FIG. 8-6   Details of vacuum insulated piping construction.

through longer lines with minimum pressure drop and vaporization. A liquefied gas transfer system is shown in Figure 8-5.

The simplest and least expensive, but not the most effective, form of insulated pipeline utilizes porous insulating materials. Polystyrene or polyurethane foams or foamed nitrile rubber perform well in this application.

A more satisfactory method of pipeline insulation is the use of vacuum insulated piping of the type shown in Figure 8-6. Such piping must be designed to permit differential expansion of the inner and outer tubes; this was formerly accomplished with flexible bellows in conjunction with powder-vacuum insula-

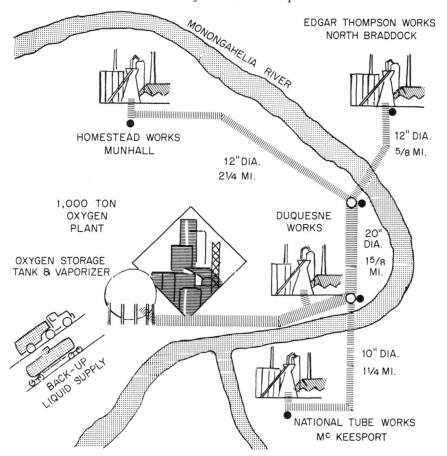

FIG. 8-7 1,000 ton capacity oxygen plant linked by 4½ mile pipeline to 4 steel mills.

tion. It is now effected by use of an Invar inside pipe having a very low coefficient of thermal expansion, which is separated from the stainless steel jacket by layers of Superinsulation.

Another type of pipeline for cryogenic gases is shown in Figure 8-7. In this case the distribution area covers several square miles, so that transmission of the cryogenic substance in the liquid state is impractical. Therefore it is distributed as a gas from a separation center, a type of system which is rapidly coming into use.

VALVES

Valves for cryogenic systems present a number of specific design problems. They should not allow heat to leak into the cryogenic transfer line. They should be simple and reliable, and should offer minimum resistance to flow. They should also be compatible with various types of insulated storage vessels and pipelines.

One design is the extended-stem valve shown in Figure 8-8. The packing area is separated from the low temperature area by the long stem. A commercial valve body may be used and fitted with an adapter containing the extending stem. In hydrogen or helium service the stem may be enclosed within a vacuum jacket.

Another useful type of valve is the so-called broken-stem valve shown in Figure 8-9. Here the heat leakage effect is minimized by having metal-to-metal contact in the stem only during valve actuation; after actuation, the handle is withdrawn.

CONTAINERS

Containers for cryogenic fluids were once spherical or cylindrical double-walled vessels of the type of the original Dewar flask. They were fragile, bulky and difficult to transport. Since that time, great progress has been made in the transport and storage of cryogenic fluids. Improved insulation has resulted in durable, compact containers which can be airborne, or which can be designed for huge truck and railway shipments, and can assure minimum losses of the cold fluids even in long term storage.

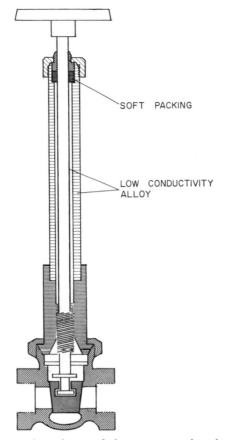

FIG. 8-8   Section of extended stem cryogenic valve.

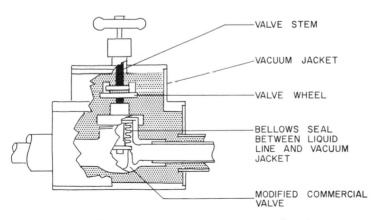

FIG. 8-9   Section of broken stem cryogenic valve.

Dewars

Early metal containers for liquid air, oxygen, and nitrogen were built on the Dewar principle. They consisted of a spherical liquid container in a spherical casing, with a long neck tube of small diameter that was made of a material of low heat conductivity. Evaporation through the neck tube reduced heat conductivity down the tube. The neck tube did double duty as a support for the dewar and as a means of filling and discharging. Such a container is shown in Figure 8-10. Figure 8-11 shows a more modern container for liquid oxygen or nitrogen which utilizes powder-vacuum insulation.

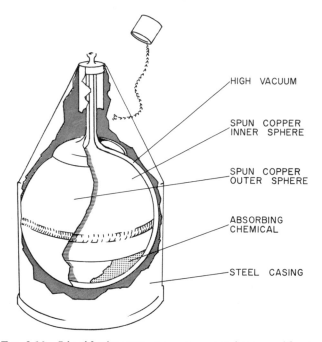

HIGH VACUUM

SPUN COPPER
INNER SPHERE

SPUN COPPER
OUTER SPHERE

ABSORBING
CHEMICAL

STEEL CASING

Fig. 8-10   Liquid nitrogen or oxygen container — older type.

When one takes the next step down in temperature to the liquid hydrogen-helium-neon range, one finds that effective dewar construction requires the use of a multiple-walled vessel. The helium container, for example, is surrounded by a vacuum con-

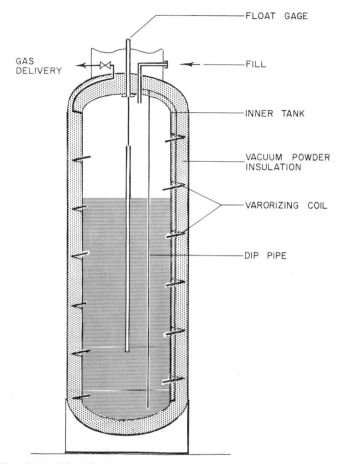

FLOAT GAGE

GAS
DELIVERY

FILL

INNER TANK

VACUUM POWDER
INSULATION

VARORIZING COIL

DIP PIPE

FIG. 8-11   Liquid nitrogen or oxygen container — newer type.

tainer and then by a double-walled vessel containing a liquid
nitrogen shield, as shown in Figure 8-12. Just as powder-vacuum
insulation has made possible simpler and more compact containers
for nitrogen and oxygen, so Superinsulation has made possible
improved hydrogen containers as shown in Figure 8-13.

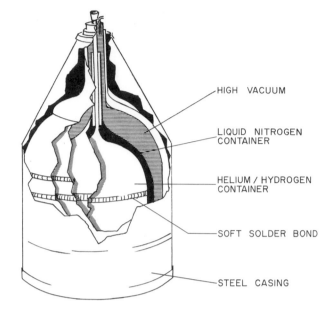

FIG. 8-12   Liquid hydrogen or helium containers — older type.

Trucks

The first truck-borne cryogenic units were huge cylindrical dewars mounted on trucks as shown in Figure 8-14. The increasing requirements of customers for cryogenic gases has led to the development of a liquid transport truck specially equipped for the delivery of high pressure gas. Such a truck is shown in Figure 8-15. As shown there, liquid from the tank on the truck is boosted in pressure by a reciprocating pump (driven by the truck motor through a gear train) and then vaporized by exchange of heat with the cooling water from the truck engine.

Trucks and tractor-trailer units can also be used for delivery of cryogenic liquids in liquid form. A tractor-trailer unit for liquid hydrogen delivery is shown in Figure 8-16. More than 500 trucks and semitrailers are in service on United States highways handling liquid oxygen, nitrogen, argon, helium and hydrogen.

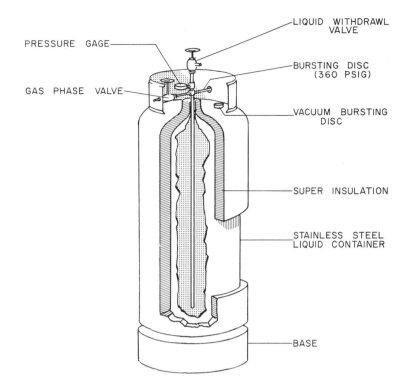

FIG. 8-13   Liquid hydrogen or helium containers — newer type.

FIG. 8-14   Old style dewar-on-a-truck transport.

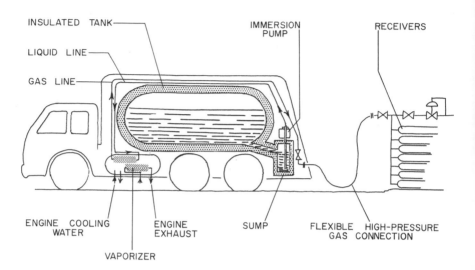

FIG. 8-15   Truck for liquid oxygen or nitrogen, showing unloading scheme.

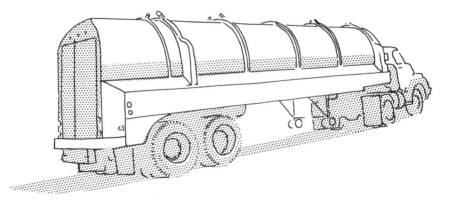

FIG. 8-16   Semi-trailer for liquid hydrogen or helium transport.

Railway Cars

The first railway tank cars for liquid oxygen shipment were put into use in 1939 to meet expanded oxygen requirements in the wartime shipbuilding program. The initial cars carried 750,-000 cubic feet (6500 gallons) of oxygen, and later designs carried one million cubic feet (8700 gallons). Figure 8-17 shows the construction of such a car. The liquid container is supported in all directions, inside an outer container, by tension rods. The space between the vessels is filled with powder-vacuum insulation. The entire car is sometimes enclosed in a standard steel box-car type structure, which affords an added degree of protection in case of train wrecks. Indeed, many such cars have been in wrecks and the liquid cargo has usually been unharmed, although the car had been severely battered. Over 500 such cars are in service in the United States today. Some newer cars, which resemble conventional tank cars, carry 1.76 million cubic feet (15,300 gallons) of oxygen, nitrogen or argon.

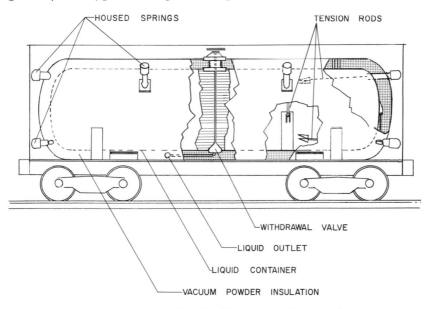

FIG. 8-17   Section of a liquid oxygen railway tank car.

A more recent development of the railway tank car for liquid cryogenic gases is the jumbo-sized car for liquid hydrogen transport shown in Figure 8-18. The new car carries 28,300 gallons of liquid hydrogen and it is designed for coast-to-coast transfer of hydrogen from production points to missile launching sites.

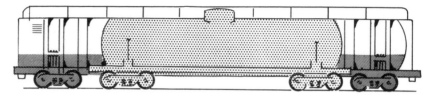

FIG. 8-18   28,300 gal. liquid hydrogen tank car, shown in comparison with standard commercial tank car.

A proposed liquid helium tank car design is shown in Figure 8-19. It has three separate containers in order to minimize losses if failure should occur. The three tanks are mounted on a 60-foot flat car.

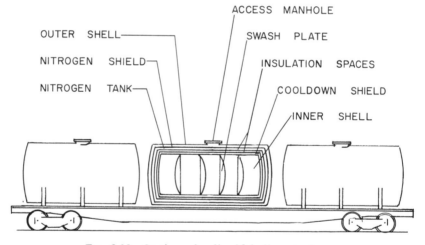

FIG. 8-19   Section of a liquid helium tank car.

Tankships

Ocean transport of cryogenic liquids was pioneered by a vessel aptly called the Methane Pioneer. Work began in 1957 on converting a 7500-ton cargo ship to a cryogenic tanker having five

6000-barrel liquid methane tanks in the hold. Aluminum containers surrounded by balsa wood insulation and an outer shell of steel are used. The insulation space is filled with nitrogen and monitored by automatic control instruments to detect leaks.

Initial shipments from Lake Charles, Louisiana to England were so successful that 170,000 barrel cryogenic tankships have been built for shipment of liquefied natural gas from the Sahara Desert to Great Britain (See Figure 8-20). The ships will be loaded at Arzew, a port near Oran in Algeria, and will be unloaded at the Gas Council storage terminal at Canvey Island in the mouth of the Thames. Here the natural gas will be regasified and delivered to seven different Gas Boards through a pipeline which will run from the neighborhood of London to that of Manchester.

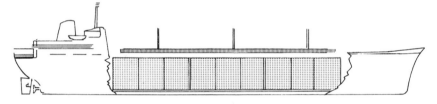

FIG. 8-20   A methane tanker (170,000 barrel).

Chapter 9

HOW COLD IS USED
—IN GAS SEPARATION

Gas separation by cryogenic means is the keystone of cryogenic processing since it is the source of many cryogenic fluids for use in science and technology. In volume of production the separation of air into its components at low temperatures is by far the most important of the separation processes.

AIR SEPARATION

Since the air around us contains about 78% of nitrogen and 21% of oxygen by volume, separation from the air is an obvious means of obtaining these gases. While oxygen is also plentiful in water, the theoretical energy for its production by electrolysis of water is about one hundred times as great as that required for its separation from air.

In the Laboratory

Laboratory units are commercially available which produce up to 4 liters per hour of high purity liquid nitrogen. Such units can be used to fill 25-liter metal dewars as shown in Figure 9-1.

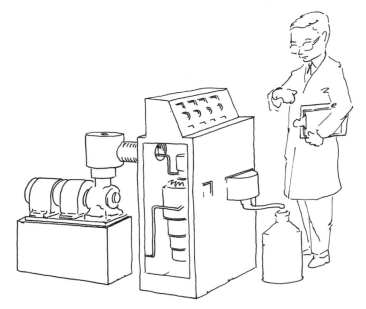

FIG. 9-1   Laboratory unit for producing liquid nitrogen.

In Large Plants

The three basic steps involved in any large air separation plant are purification, refrigeration, and separation. The process equipment available from various manufacturers differs widely, particularly in methods of removing from the entering air stream such impurities as carbon dioxide, water and hydrocarbons; methods of producing the necessary refrigeration; operating pressures; and types of distillation columns.

The purification of the air consists of the removal of any suspended solids or liquids, such as dust, dirt or droplets of hydrocarbons. Purification also includes the removal of hydrocarbon vapor, water vapor, and carbon dioxide gas. These operations are performed by mechanical filters and traps, by freezing, or by a combination of these methods, so that the air entering the refrigeration system is free of these impurities.

Refrigeration is necessary in order to liquefy the air. Incoming air is cooled to the liquefaction temperature of about —300°F (—185°C) by a combination of three methods. The first method

is heat exchange with a colder material in either heat exchangers
or regenerators. The second method is Joule-Thomson expansion
(See Figure 2-3). The third method is expansion in a turbine or
reciprocating engine (See Figure 2-5).

The operating pressure depends on whether the nitrogen and
oxygen are to be obtained in gaseous or liquid form. When
gaseous products are desired, a low-pressure cycle is used and
the products are gasified by heat exchange with the entering air.
When liquid products are desired, a high-pressure cycle is used
as shown in Figure 9-2. The external physical appearance of
such a plant is as shown in Figure 9-3.

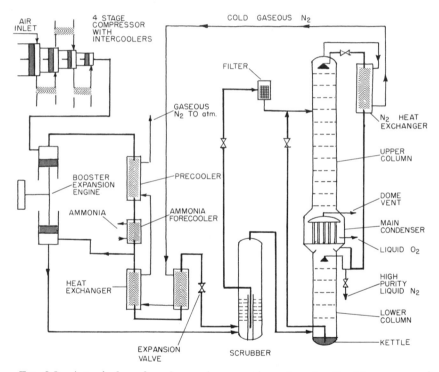

FIG. 9-2   A typical modern large air separation plant for liquid oxygen and
nitrogen.

In the separation column the vapor rises and the liquid
descends, flowing across a series of trays which are spaced throughout the column. As the gas approaches the top of the column it

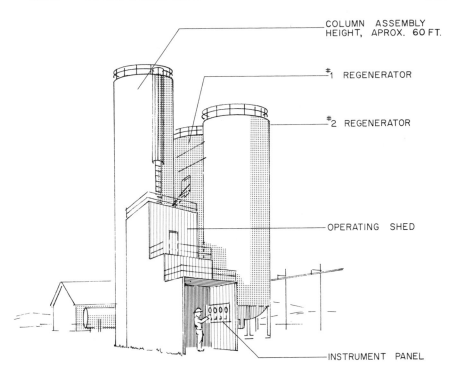

FIG. 9-3 Air separation plant producing 80 million cu. ft. of oxygen per month.

becomes richer in the lower boiling constituent, nitrogen. The liquid, as it approaches the bottom of the column, becomes richer in the higher boiling constituent, oxygen.

Instrumentation and automatic control are among the more important design features of an air separation plant. They have now been developed to such a degree that the plants can operate virtually unattended. The scheme of operation of an unattended oxygen plant is shown in Figure 9-4.

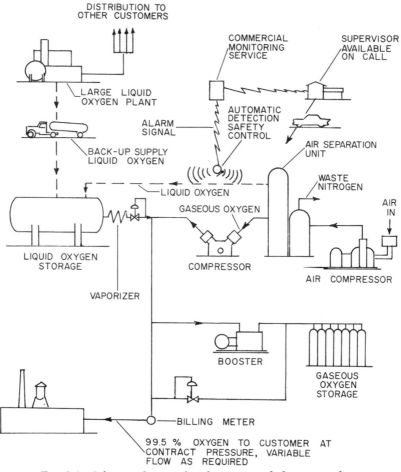

FIG. 9-4   Scheme of operation for unattended oxygen plant.

COKE OVEN GAS SEPARATION

Coke oven gas is a complex mixture having a typical composition as follows:

Hydrogen	47 — 60%
Methane	20 — 30%
Nitrogen	4 — 14%
Carbon monoxide	4 — 7%
Carbon dioxide	1 — 3%
Ethylene	1 — 3%
Ethane	1 — 2%

This mixture may be separated by low-temperature means to give an ammonia synthesis gas (75% hydrogen and 25% nitrogen). Prior to World War II about a third of the hydrogen converted to synthetic ammonia in Europe was derived from coke oven gas.

Raw coke oven gas is first scrubbed with ammonia to remove carbon dioxide and sulfur compounds. It is then cooled and dried prior to entry to the separation unit. Ethylene and propylene are extracted in the initial heat exchangers, which are cooled by product gas as shown in Figure 9-5. The main body of coke

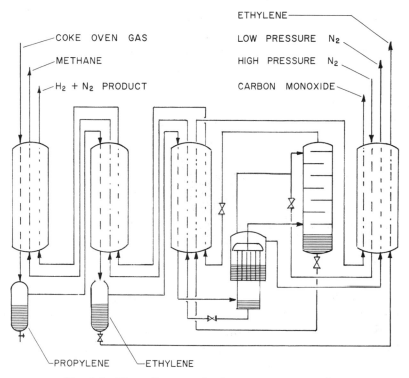

FIG. 9-5   Flow diagram of coke oven gas separation.

oven gas is then condensed by evaporation of liquid nitrogen in an evaporator. Residual gas is scrubbed with liquid nitrogen in a wash tower. The coke oven gas separation plant is thus always operated in conjunction with an air separation plant for the production of liquid nitrogen. The nitrogen is employed to fur-

nish the basic refrigeration needed, to scrub out residual impurities after separation of the components, and for use in the
synthesis gas, which is a 3:1 mixture of nitrogen and hydrogen.

HELIUM FROM NATURAL GAS

Helium is extracted from helium-bearing natural gases, which
contain 1 to 8 per cent of helium and 12 to 80 per cent of
nitrogen, the remainder consisting chiefly of methane; thus
nitrogen is a common and abundant constituent of helium-
bearing natural gases. Process pressures are as high as 2700 psi
and process temperatures range down to —310°F (—190°C).
These conditions effect liquefaction of all constituents of the gas
feed except helium, and so permit helium recovery by simple
phase separation. The process is unique in combining high
operating pressure with low operating temperatures at high gas
processing rates. Due to the low helium concentration, helium
plants have been designed to process upwards of 30 million
cubic feet of natural gas per day.

A typical pressure of natural gas as it exists in the field is about
600 psi; so that most of the refrigeration for the process is obtained
by its expansion from field pressure to about 70 psi.

In the plant as shown in Figure 9-6, the entering natural gas
is cooled by exchanging its heat with cold products in a heat
exchanger, and almost completely liquefied. It then passes to a
helium separator operating at 200 - 300 psi; the gas phase contains
about 60% helium and about 40% nitrogen, plus small amounts
of methane. The crude helium from this separator is compressed
to 2700 psi and sent to a separator cooled by liquid nitrogen,
which condenses almost all the nitrogen, leaving production-
grade helium of 98.5 per cent purity. This helium may be further
purified to 99.7 per cent by passage through activated charcoal
beds at liquid nitrogen temperatures.

High-pressure nitrogen is required to feed such a helium-
extraction plant at the startup, but the nitrogen liquefaction plant
built into the cycle is kept supplied with nitrogen extracted from
the natural gas.

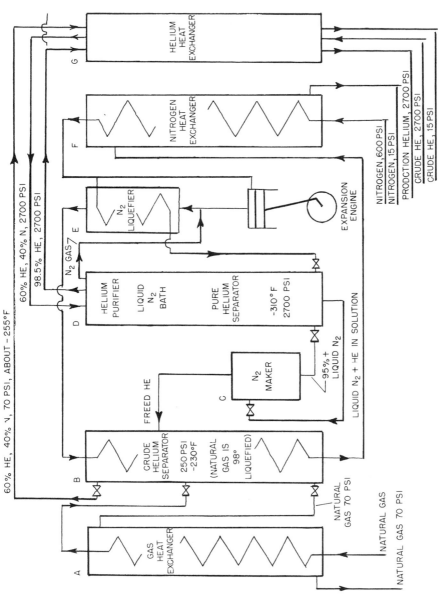

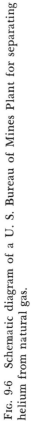

FIG. 9-6 Schematic diagram of a U. S. Bureau of Mines Plant for separating helium from natural gas.

HELIUM-3 FROM HELIUM-4

Natural helium consists of two isotopes, helium-4 and helium-3, the latter being present only in very low concentrations. It constitutes about 1 part per million of helium of atmospheric origin, and about one part in ten million of helium extracted from natural gas. Helium-3 is also a product of the radioactive decay of tritium, and can be separated easily from tritium by the use of a palladium membrane.

Helium-3 is of particular cryogenic interest because, at a given temperature, the vapor pressure of liquid helium-3 is much higher than that of ordinary helium-4. Thus, whereas pumping on helium-4 permits attainment of a temperature of 0.8°K, pumping on helium-3 permits one to reach 0.3°K.

Separation of the two helium isotopes may be accomplished by thermal diffusion or other well-known methods of isotope separation. An even better procedure is the combination of an isotope enrichment method based on superfluidity, with a subsequent fractional distillation, in an apparatus of the type shown in Figure 9-7. When a temperature gradient is produced by a heating coil in helium below 2.2°K, helium-4 atoms move toward the heat source. Helium-3 does not exhibit the phenomenon of superfluidity and moves away from the heating coil to the colder region of the helium separation vessel. The helium-3 is said to be "heat-flushed" away from helium-4. Enrichment factors as high as 30,000 have been reported for this method. Subsequent distillation can produce almost pure helium-3.

DEUTERIUM FROM ORDINARY HYDROGEN

The demand for heavy water as a moderator in nuclear reactors as well as the need for deuterium as a raw material for thermonuclear fusion reactions has stimulated interest in processes for deuterium production. Deuterium (heavy hydrogen or hydrogen-2) occurs in natural hydrogen to the extent of one part in

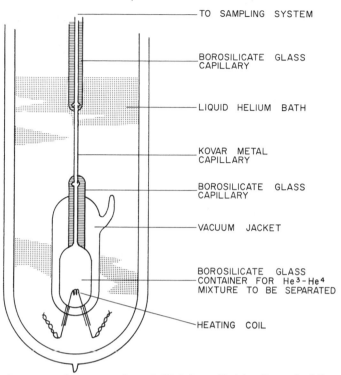

TO SAMPLING SYSTEM

BOROSILICATE GLASS
CAPILLARY

LIQUID HELIUM BATH

KOVAR METAL
CAPILLARY

BOROSILICATE GLASS
CAPILLARY

VACUUM JACKET

BOROSILICATE GLASS
CONTAINER FOR He^3-He^4
MIXTURE TO BE SEPARATED

HEATING COIL

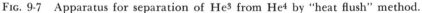

Fig. 9-7   Apparatus for separation of He^3 from He^4 by "heat flush" method.

6900, the remainder being protium (hydrogen-1). The principal methods which have been considered for the separation of these hydrogen isotopes are:

1. Catalytic exchange between water and water vapor.
2. Distillation of water.
3. Distillation of liquid hydrogen.

The distillation of liquid hydrogen was originally rejected as a method of obtaining deuterium because of the lack of design data and because of the problems expected to arise in operation at $20°K$. However, in light of present-day cryogenic knowledge, design parameters are available for the process shown in Figure 9-8.

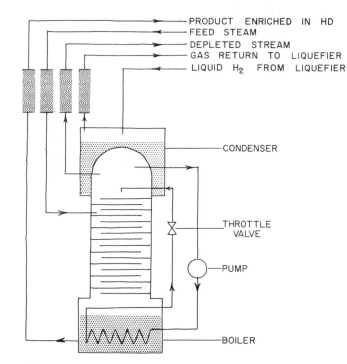

PRODUCT ENRICHED IN HD
FEED STEAM
DEPLETED STREAM
GAS RETURN TO LIQUEFIER
LIQUID H_2 FROM LIQUEFIER

CONDENSER

THROTTLE VALVE

PUMP

BOILER

FIG. 9-8   Flow diagram column for separation of HD from natural hydrogen.

Since the heavy isotope occurs as HD rather than D_2, the initial step is concentration of HD by two-stage distillation. The resulting product is then catalyzed to achieve equilibrium between H_2, HD and D_2, and pure D_2 is obtained in a final distillation step.

Chapter 10

HOW COLD IS USED
—AS A SOURCE OF GASES

Cryogenic liquids are a compact and versatile source of gases, which are available at low pressures by simple vaporization or at high pressures by boosting the pressure on the liquid and then vaporizing it.

Production of gas from the liquid may be gradual or it may be almost explosive. High pressure nitrogen can be used explosively in coal mining in a system analogous to those using air or carbon dioxide. However, while this use of nitrogen is technically feasible, its economics are doubtful.

NITROGEN FOR OUR WELLS

Acidizing, fracturing, perforating, drill stem testing and the injection of treating fluids are all oil-field operations requiring high gas flows at high pressures for short periods (30 minutes or so).

Why nitrogen? One advantage is its non-flammability as compared to air when working with hydrocarbon gases at high pressures. Another reason is the feasibility of providing large volumes of gas on demand by pumping liquid nitrogen to high pressure and then vaporizing it; the apparatus for such an operation is much simpler than the huge batteries of air compressors needed to supply air in equivalent volume at equivalent pressure.

Assuming that a typical well treatment requires 800,000 cubic feet of nitrogen and assuming 1000 such operations per month, there would be a market for 800 million cubic feet of nitrogen per month or about 1000 tons per day.

The preceding estimates may be high because one commercial organization engaged in well treating reports that 150,000 cubic feet per well is an economic maximum for acidizing and fracturing. This quantity, if sufficient, is convenient because 6 tons of liquid nitrogen, the capacity of a standard truck, yields 186,000 cubic feet of gas.

What then are the specific well treating operations where nitrogen can be used to advantage?

One such operation is acidizing, in which some nitrogen is run into the well ahead of the acid and more nitrogen along with the acid. Because of its low solubility, the nitrogen occurs as gas bubbles in the acid. When the acid action is complete, the pressure on the well is released and the nitrogen bubbles expand and force the acid out of the strata and up the well bore with a gas-lift effect, producing a clear well in record time. A well in which nitrogen has been used as an aid in acidizing can be back in production within 2-3 hours after acidizing, whereas swabbing methods take several days to clear a well (See Figure 10-1).

Perforating can be carried out better in an empty casing than in a mud-filled casing. After a well has been drilled, an explosive-bearing perforating gun is lowered and used to open holes into the oil-bearing formation (See Figure 10-2). Sometimes fluids from the casing are forced into the formation, which may hinder production for the life of the well. When perforating from a dry hole under nitrogen pressure, one does not run this danger. After perforation is complete, the gun is withdrawn and nitrogen pressure is slowly reduced to bring in the well (See also Figure 10-3).

Drill stem testing uses nitrogen to better advantage than water in a hydrostatic test. Since the industry is constantly drilling deeper wells, with consequent higher well-head pressures, the detection of gas leaks which could cause fires has become increasingly important. Testing with high pressure nitrogen is perhaps

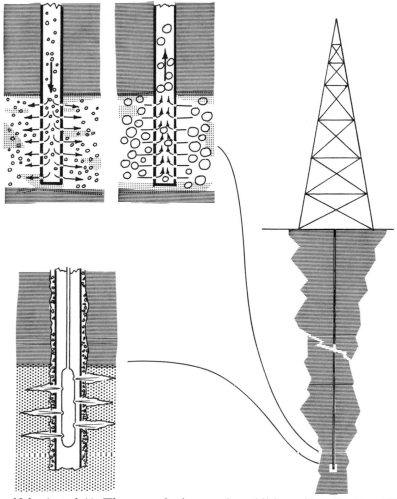

FIG. 10-1 (*top left*) The use of nitrogen in acidizing oil wells. FIG. 10-2 (*bottom left*) Use of nitrogen in perforating oil wells.

the safest and most efficient way to find such leaks. After drill stem testing is complete, fluid sampling is improved because there is no mud in the drill stem to contaminate the samples. (See Figure 10-4.)

Nitrogen is also used for injection of treating fluids into wells. When inhibitors are forced into the formation, they may be left there to be removed along with the normal flow of oil and gas,

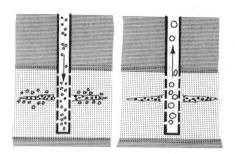

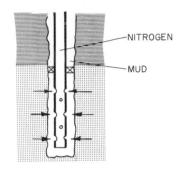

FIG. 10-3   The use of nitrogen in frac-   FIG. 10-4   Use of nitrogen in
turing oil wells.   drill stem testing.

rather than removed immediately as in the case of acid or fracture
fluids. When nitrogen gas is used, inhibitors can be placed rapidly
with no damage to the face of the formation (See Figure 10-5).

Electric logging can also benefit if it is conducted in a mud-free
hole. Unwanted fluids can be displaced from a well neatly and
efficiently by using nitrogen as shown in Figure 10-6.

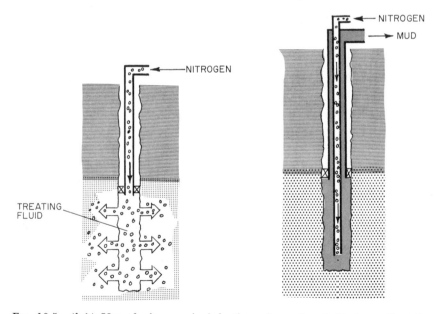

FIG. 10-5   (left) Use of nitrogen in injection of treating fluids into oil wells.
FIG. 10-6   (right) Displacement of unwanted fluids by nitrogen.

Sampling of formations at various depths can be carried out precisely by controlled release of nitrogen pressure to effect the release of small quantities of fluid into the hole from the various zones.

Well completion can be carried out under safe and controlled conditions by gradual release of nitrogen pressure.

Still another possibility is the drilling of wells under nitrogen pressure. This is perhaps more remote economically than the proven treating operations described above. If it should materialize, it could consume a very great amount of nitrogen. Air drilling has been used commercially in mud-free operations, and nitrogen-drilling would be safer than air drilling, with the added convenience of providing large volumes of high pressure gas at the well-head by the use of simple equipment.

Another potential application of nitrogen is its use for sweeping pipelines in the field. Its justification is increased safety due to the avoidance of flammable hydrocarbon-air mixtures. Further, it has actually been found possible to sandblast pipeline interiors at high nitrogen flow rates.

Even prospecting for oil may be aided by nitrogen. A technique has been visualized whereby oil is found by pumping nitrogen into the ground and "sniffing" the gas leaking up from the area for traces of hydrocarbons.

HYDROGEN FOR BALLOONS IN FLIGHT

Meteorological balloons must often be operated at constant altitudes up to 100,000 feet for several days at a time to insure adequate data collection. During the day, the gas expands from the solar heating and is exhausted from the balloon. At night the gas contracts and the balloon would descend unless additional lift were provided. This counteracting effect could be obtained by dropping ballast, but the weight of ballast necessary would be excessive, amounting to perhaps 30 to 40% of the gross load of the balloon. In an attempt to cut the weight required for operation at constant altitude, the possibility of supplying hydrogen at operating altitude was investigated. It quickly became apparent that the weight penalty from the use of gaseous hydrogen in high-pressure cylinders was greater than that from using disposable ballast as a means of stabilization. Attention then turned to the use of liquid hydrogen in a dewar as the source of the required gas. This proved to be the desired solution and resulted in the design shown in Figure 10-7.

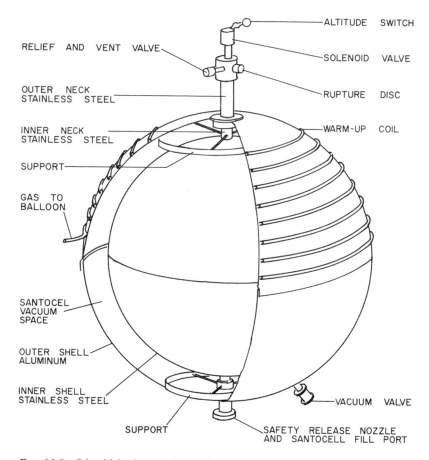

FIG. 10-7 Liquid hydrogen dewar for supplying gas to balloons in flight.

OXYGEN SUPPLY FOR AIRCRAFT PERSONNEL

Liquid oxygen is now a standard source of oxygen for pilots and crewmen in high-altitude operations of the United States Air Force. It is used instead of gaseous oxygen because of appreciable weight and space savings effected the use of a cryogenic liquid instead of a gas. There is a weight reduction of 65 per cent and a space reduction of 85%, since one volume of the liquid can be converted to over 800 volumes of oxygen gas suitable for breathing. The alternatives to the use of liquid would be a large number of gas containers holding oxygen at moderate pressure or a few heavy containers holding oxygen at very high pressure.

The use of liquid oxygen in aircraft is not new and early trials date back to 1921. Indeed, technical papers discussing this topic at some length were presented at a symposium on "Generation and Utilization of Cold" before the Faraday Society in London in October of 1922. Development of a really practical system for the conversion of the cold liquid oxygen to a gas at ambient temperature (called a "cold converter") was not achieved, however, until about 1940. Such a system uses no external source of energy other than heat from the atmosphere. The aircraft cold converter for oxygen is not too dissimilar to the hydrogen dewar shown in Figure 10-7.

Chapter 11

HOW COLD IS USED
— IN SPACE RESEARCH

It seems difficult to reconcile much of space research with cryogenics. We see fiery rocket exhausts appearing at test stands in the desert and streaking back from missiles leaving Cape Canaveral for space. We hear of the thermal barrier and of beryllium heat shields to keep space pilots from being cooked on re-entry. All of these high temperature phenomena seem a far cry from the world of low temperatures.

However, space research is a major consumer of the cryogenic fluids, using oxygen as a chemical reactant, hydrogen both as a chemical fuel and also as a working medium for nuclear rockets, nitrogen for precooling, flushing and cold flow testing of rockets on the test stands and for cooling of space simulator chambers, and helium for cryopumping of space simulator chambers.

IN MISSILE LAUNCHING

Cryogenic fluids are the most important factors in a successful missile launch, aside from the missile engine itself and the control mechanism. While solid propellants have been the subject of much discussion and certainly will find application in tactical weapons for use in the field, liquid propellants still **move** most of our

116

major missiles, and those of other nations as well, off the launch pad and into space.

Cryogenic liquids are used to test, precool and flush the piping in a typical rocket test stand such as that shown in Figure 11-1. They are used in propellant transfer, and they constitute the propellants themselves.

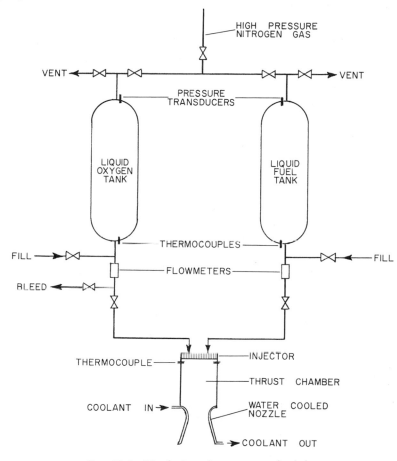

Fig. 11-1 Typical rocket test stand piping.

For Personnel Protection in Fuel Handling

One of the problems which has been attacked by the United States Army Ballistic Missile Program has been the development of clothing to protect liquid fuel handlers from the harmful effects of spills and to prevent the inhalation of toxic fumes. A major development was the totally enclosed, impermeable suit, equipped with gloves and gas mask. This then posed problems of cooling the wearer within the suit to relieve heat stress, especially in hot climates; and of supplying a source of pure air for breathing. These problems were solved by a back-pack containing liquid air as shown in Figure 11-2. This device cools the suit, furnishes oxygen for breathing, maintains a positive pressure within the suit to keep toxic fumes from entering, and prevents fogging of the face piece in the mask. The entire system weighs about 17 pounds.

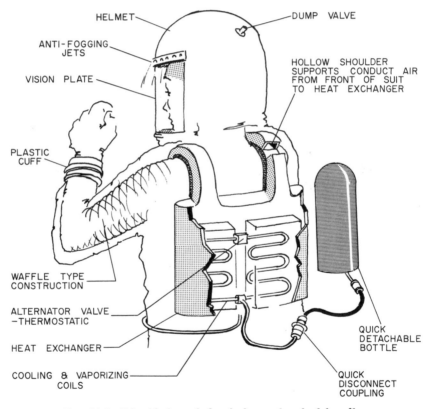

FIG. 11-2   Liquid-air-cooled suit for rocket fuel handlers.

In Precooling and Flushing

One source has estimated that 150 tons per day of liquid nitrogen are used in propellent transfer operations. They include the precooling of tanks and piping from ambient temperatures to cryogenic temperatures, and flushing of lines. For these purposes liquid nitrogen has the advantages of relatively low cost and chemical inertness.

In Cold Flow Testing

The testing of missile parts that are to be in contact with liquid oxygen is usually performed in liquid nitrogen. This permits testing in the cryogenic temperature range without hazard. It has been estimated that 150 tons per day of liquid nitrogen were consumed during 1962 in such testing.

In Propellant Pressurizing Systems

Gaseous nitrogen was used to pressurize the alcohol fuel tank in the German V-2 rocket; it was also used to pressurize the hydrogen peroxide and calcium permanganate reactor which generated steam to drive the turbine which powered the main fuel pumps.

Nitrogen remains the material of choice in later generations of rockets for pressurizing reactive materials. Now that techniques have been developed for storage and transport of liquid nitrogen, one is more likely to consider using liquid nitrogen as the source of nitrogen gas under pressure for propellant transfer.

In Vehicle Cooling

High speed flight in relatively dense atmospheres near the earth, encountered in supersonic aircraft or in space vehicle re-entry, poses severe cooling problems due to the heat entering through the vehicle skin from the hot boundary layer, plus the heat generated within the vehicle by electrical and other equipment. In contrast to subsonic flight with propellor-driven aircraft, the ambient air is not available for cooling.

A possible solution to this problem is the use of a cryogenic liquid coolant, which also pressurizes the instrument compartment and supplies the power necessary for its operation. Such a system could be designed to handle a cooling load of 15 kilowatts, to weigh less than 5 pounds, and to be about the size of a grapefruit.

The selection of a specific cryogenic coolant for such a system requires a compromise between a number of factors — the storage space required, which is determined by the specific gravity of the coolant; the heat exchanger surface required; the power generation capability per unit of coolant; and the availability, corrosiveness, and combustibility of the coolant.

A specific cryogenic cooling application is found in the X-15 research airplane, where liquid nitrogen is used for cooling and pressurizing the airplane cabin and equipment bay.

As Auxiliary Power Source

Cryogenic liquids can be used to power two different kinds of auxiliary power sources.

One type is a liquid-nitrogen hydraulic system, as shown in Figure 11-3, in which liquid nitrogen is heated and used to drive a motor. The motor in turn drives a nitrogen pump and also furnishes power for other purposes.

A second type of auxiliary power source using cryogenic liquids is the fuel cell, in which both fuel and oxidizer are

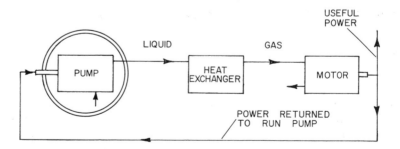

FIG. 11-3   Auxiliary power system for space vehicle using liquid nitrogen.

liquids, such as liquid hydrogen and liquid oxygen. The first operational use of such a power source in the United States will occur in the two-man Gemini space vehicle. An ion-exchange membrane fuel cell utilizing hydrogen and oxygen will deliver a peak load of almost 2 kilowatts to operate electrical equipment while the craft streaks through space. A useful by-product is the pint of drinking water produced for every kilowatt hour of operation to augment the water supply carried in the spacecraft.

In Cryostorable Missile Systems

The problem of maintaining constant missile readiness to permit one to answer a warning of an aggressor's attack within minutes is critical in any nation's planning. While it has been thought by some that solid-propellant motors are the only answer to this problem, this is not necessarily the case. In fact, considerable thought has been given to maintaining missiles fueled by cryogenic propellants in a state of constant readiness. Such a development would give the advantage of instant readiness in a missile having the superior impulse capabilities of the liquid-propellant type of rocket motor.

To maintain a cryogenic missile in constant readiness would involve some such scheme as that shown in Figure 11-4. Here, clam-shell tanks containing liquid nitrogen enclose the missile and keep the stored propellants cool. When ready to fire the clam-shell opens and the missile is moved into firing position.

As Propellants

The concept of using a cryogenic liquid as a rocket propellant is attractive for several reasons:

(1) Storage and handling as a compact liquid is the easiest and most efficient way of handling a material which is to generate many times its volume of propellant gas.

(2) Liquid propellant motors offer higher specific impulse values (pounds of thrust produced per pound of propellant consumed per second) than do solid propellant motors.

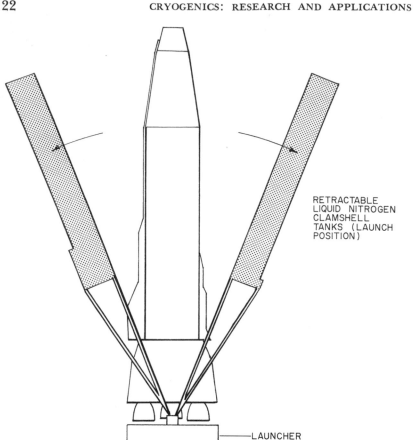

RETRACTABLE
LIQUID NITROGEN
CLAMSHELL
TANKS (LAUNCH
POSITION)

—————LAUNCHER

FIG. 11-4   Cryostorable liquid fuel missile.

(3) The materials with the most desirable characteristics
    (low molecular weight of exhaust products, for exam-
    ple) are liquids only at cryogenic temperatures —
    hydrogen, for instance.

(4) The possibility of new exotic propellants based on
    unstable molecular species will certainly necessitate
    their handling and storage at cryogenic temperatures
    for reasons of stability.

In Chemical Rockets. Most chemical rockets have bipropellant
systems containing a fuel and an oxidizer. The oxidizer which has
found greatest application is liquid oxygen, although development

work has been done on the more powerful, but more corrosive and difficult to handle, liquid fluorine. Liquid oxygen is the work horse among rocket oxidizers. It has been used since the beginning of modern rocketry, in Professor R. H. Goddard's experiments and later by the Germans in the V-2. Today all big modern United States launch vehicles use liquid oxygen as the oxidant. Materials and equipment have been devised to make oxygen handling safe and trouble-free; 2000 tons per day of liquid oxygen are used in missile operations in the United States.

While the fuels for the big rockets have been non-cryogenic fluids in many cases, the trend is to higher energy propellants and specifically to liquid hydrogen. The German V-2 bombardment rocket was able to operate satisfactorily on 75% ethyl alcohol as a fuel, but the Atlas and Thor use purified kerosene in their launch stages. Tomorrow's more powerful and sophisticated rockets such as the Nova shown in Figure 11-5 will use kerosene in the launch stage but liquid hydrogen in the upper stages.

One of the few disadvantages of hydrogen is its low density, which makes large, bulky tanks necessary to store it in the rocket booster. Experiments are being conducted on the cooling of liquid hydrogen by liquid helium to produce a hydrogen "slush," that is, a mixture of solid and liquid hydrogen. This viscous material is considerably greater in density than the liquid, so that more hydrogen may be carried in the propellant tanks.

In the Aerospaceplane. A unique concept is under development by the United States Air Force involving the combination of three types of engines in a single vehicle. It will have turbojet engines for takeoff and power-on landings, and for acceleration to supersonic speeds. For further acceleration (up to Mach 5 or Mach 10) it will use ramjet engines, which may be combined with the turbojet engines in a turboramjet configuration. Finally, it will use rocket engines burning liquid hydrogen by combustion in liquid oxygen, which is collected from the atmosphere during the supersonic cruise phase, liquefied and separated on board, and stored. This third power plant would boost the plane through Mach 18 to orbital speeds. Thus the aerospaceplane would be essentially a hydrogen tank with wings, having the capability

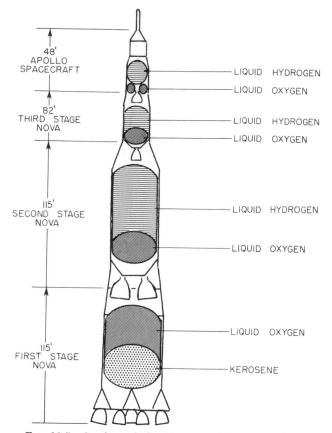

FIG. 11-5   Section of the Nova-Apollo spacecraft.

of taking off in a conventional manner, going into orbit, and returning to a base anywhere on earth.

In Rockets Using Metastable Atoms as Fuels. The possibility of attaining specific impulse values an order of magnitude greater than those obtainable from chemical fuels lies in the use of atoms or molecules in metastable states of higher energy (also called "excited" states).

Metastable helium is one attractive possibility. This is helium in which one of the two electrons occupies a higher energy orbit and moves roughly parallel to the other electron, which is in its usual orbit. One problem is to produce this metastable helium at a low temperature (indications are that this can be done by excitation by radio waves) and another problem is to store it so its energy is not released until needed. A third problem is to find a way to activate it at low temperatures to release its energy. Workers at the Redstone Arsenal at Huntsville, Alabama have calculated that this material has a theoretical specific impulse of 2900, which is more than 10 times greater than the alcohol-oxygen mixture used in the German V-2.

Another possibility is the utilization of hydrogen atoms with like electron spins (See Figure 7-4) which would not combine to form molecules. (As was noted in Chapter 7, two atoms having opposite electron spins join to form hydrogen molecules.) It might be possible to apply a magnetic separation technique to separate the two species. As in the case of metastable helium, storing these atoms would present another difficult problem. If these production and storage problems could be solved, the high specific impulse obtainable from this material, and the ease of producing hydrogen, could lead to very widespread use of an atomic hydrogen motor.

In Nuclear Rockets. In addition to its use as a most important fuel in chemical rockets, hydrogen might also be used as a working fluid in a vehicle that obtained its energy from another source, for example, a nuclear reactor. Specific impulse values in the range of 600 to 800 have been calculated for nuclear reactors — nearly double those obtainable with the best chemical propellant combinations.

A joint program of the U. S. Atomic Energy Commission (AEC) and the National Aeronautics and Space Agency (NASA) has been conducted under the name of Project Rover at the AEC proving ground at Jackass Flats, Nevada, having as its goal the development of a hydrogen-fueled nuclear rocket engine. The prototype engine was called the Kiwi after the flightless bird found in New Zealand.

The program is proceeding after successful Kiwi tests were made, first with gaseous and then with liquid hydrogen. Now a National Nuclear Rocket Development Station has been built at Jackass Flats to test the Nerva (Nuclear Engine for Rocket Vehicle Application) engine so that rocket components will be tested in an environment similar to that in a full-power nuclear engine run (See Figure 11-6). Then the Rift (Reactor in flight test) will involve a test of a complete nuclear stage of a rocket atop an advanced Saturn booster. The ultimate product of this program is to be a rocket such as that shown in Figure 1-10.

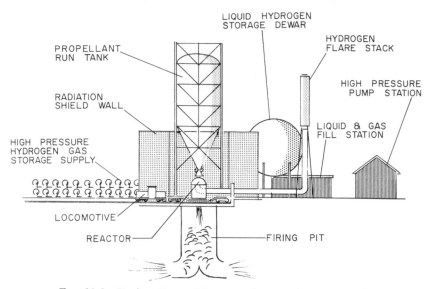

FIG. 11-6   Project Rover Nerva nuclear engine test stand.

IN SPACE SIMULATORS

In these early years of manned space flight, much testing must be done on components and even on complete spacecraft under conditions duplicating the environment of a given mission.

One of the most important of these conditions is that of temperature under the near-vacuum pressures of deep space, where the temperature of a body depends on the heat it loses by radiation from its surface and the heat it gains from radiation entering it. The cold of deep space, that is due to the loss of heat by radiation, is simulated by cooling the walls of the test object by means of liquid nitrogen or other cryogenic fluids, while the heat gained from incident solar radiation is simulated by lamps.

Simulation of the vacuum of outer space, which may be as low as 10^{-14} torricelli (millimeters of mercury) is difficult. Attainment of such low pressures would be highly uneconomic by use of conventional vacuum pumps, even if possible. To solve this problem, the methods of cryogenics have produced a new technique called cryopumping, which is discussed later in this chapter.

Nitrogen Refrigerators

The heat loss from an object in outer space is equivalent to that through a wall having a temperature of 3 - 4°K. Space duplication would require that a space chamber wall be at that temperature. Space simulation, on the other hand, only requires that the surrounding wall temperature be reduced to the point where radiation returned to the test vehicle be small compared to that radiated by the vehicle. A wall temperature of 100°K (easy to attain by using nitrogen, which boils at 77°K) returns only about one per cent of the total energy radiated from a test vehicle at 300°K, and thus represents adequate simulation of deep space.

The liquid nitrogen-cooled walls of space simulator chambers provide a major use for nitrogen. Consumption of a typical chamber of the current vintage may be 20 tons of nitrogen per day, and the larger models being built will consume as much as 100 tons per day. For the 30 or more of these around the United States, the daily consumption of liquid nitrogen for this use alone is perhaps 500 tons per day now and could reach 2000 tons per day by 1970.

Space simulator chambers are made in all manner of sizes and shapes. One handy variety is advertised as providing "instant outerspace" for the testing of component hardware under controlled conditions of vibration (both random and shock-wave), vacuum (10^{-8} torricelli), temperature (a cold wall cooled by liquid nitrogen at —320°F) and incoming solar radiation. Electrical, electronic, hydraulic, pneumatic and cryogenic capabilities are provided in one small chamber.

Helium Cryopumps

Only carbon dioxide, water vapor, and hydrocarbons are removed by nitrogen refrigerated walls. To obtain the really high-vacuum of 10^{-14} torr., we need a means of removing oxygen, nitrogen and argon as well. Cryopumping was invented in about 1957 to meet this need.

Cryopumping can be accomplished by placing a helium-cooled cryopanel within a space simulation chamber, or it may be effected by using vacuum pumps to draw the gas over liquid helium-filled cooling fins. In this way the vapor pressures of all gases except hydrogen are reduced to negligible values by the use of liquid helium refrigeration. Figure 11-7 shows a helium

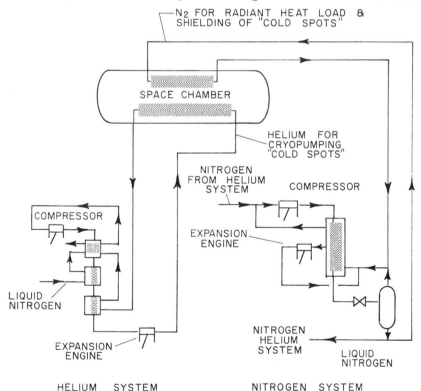

FIG. 11-7   Space simulation chamber fundamentals with nitrogen cooling and helium cryopumping.

cryopanel used in conjunction with liquid nitrogen cooling in a space simulation chamber.

The difficulties of obtaining very high (or "hard") vacuum are apparent if we consider the pressures obtainable by various equipment. Mechanical vacuum pumps of the laboratory type can exhaust a system from atmospheric pressure of 760 torr. down to about 1.0 torr. Diffusion pumps can go half way to the hard vacuum figure of 10^{-14} torr., or to about 10^{-7} torr. Cryopumping goes further — down to 10^{-10} to 10^{-12} torr.

Firing tests of plasma engines pose the additional problems of preventing the engine exhaust products from destroying the high vacuum in the space simulation chamber. Cryopanels take care of this problem by trapping the engine exhaust products and so preventing both loss of vacuum and contamination of the chamber by the exhaust products. It is necessary of course to

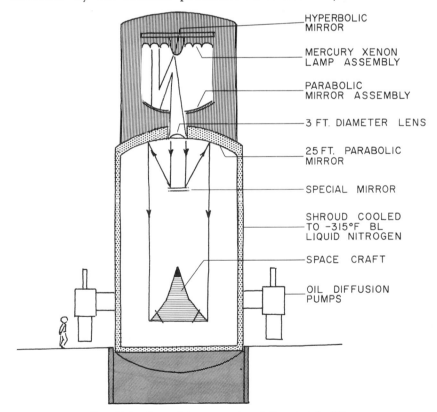

FIG. 11-8   Complete space simulation test facility.

"defrost" the cryopanel periodically and to remove the condensate from the test chamber.

Proof that only cryogenic pumping can handle such firing tests is given by the fact that even a rocket having only a ten-pound thrust at a simulated altitude of 100 miles would require pumps costing hundreds of millions of dollars and using millions of kilowatts of electrical energy, both of which are prohibitive (especially the electrical energy requirement). At a pressure of 10^{-6} torr. in the chamber, such a test would involve moving 3×10^{10} cubic feet of gas per minute.

It can also be calculated that two-thirds of an acre of surface cooled by liquid nitrogen is necessary to test a cesium ion engine of only one-pound thrust. Cryogenics make the figures manageable, but they are still formidable.

Figure 11-8 shows a complete space test facility with provisions for simulating vacuum, temperature and radiation conditions.

Chapter 12

HOW COLD IS USED—IN BIOLOGY

The use of cold in biology has given birth to a new subscience — cryobiology. This is the study of life in relation to cold.

Cold is frequently regarded as a killing agent — the association between exposure to cold and human life brings to mind headlines such as "Man frozen to death in subzero cold." Now as our insight deepens, cold is becoming more widely known and used as a preserver rather than a destroyer of life. Artificial insemination of cattle using bull semen preserved at liquid nitrogen temperatures is now a standard commercial practice. Blood preservation by freezing is undergoing extensive clinical trials, and successful cryosurgery has been reported. Banking of human organs at liquid nitrogen temperatures as spare parts in surgery is a hope for tomorrow.

As man ventures into space, cryobiology assumes new importance. As one authority has put it, "To go beyond the solar system, we must send families — or we must freeze people." This is because man may not be able to stand the rigors of extended space travel — and even if he can — the length of the trip may exceed his total normal life span. If transported in a state of frozen suspended animation, he may be able to arrive at his destination decades after blast-off, as young and vigorous as the day he departed. Cryogenics thus offers for the first time the opportunity of stopping and starting the biological clock at will and achieving suspended animation — an age-old dream which has found expression heretofore only in such places as the works of Jules Verne.

In nearer explorations of space in the more immediate time to come, cryobiology is essential to the return of plants, spores, and even animals from other planets. The first test may well come in bringing spores to the earth from the moon, which is a strong possibility for the first trip.

The foundations for the development of methods for the freezing of whole animals have recently been laid by Dr. Audrey Smith and her co-workers at the National Institute for Medical Research at Mill Hill in London, England. They have succeeded in cooling golden hamsters at $-5°C$ to the point where 50 to 60% of the water content of the brain, for example, was transformed to ice. No protective additives of any kind were fed to the hamsters, but when they were rewarmed within one hour after freezing they recovered completely.

The pioneer in exploration of the biological effects of low temperatures was the Italian priest and biologist, Lazaro Spallanzani. As long ago as 1780-90, he recorded observations on the effects of low temperatures on insects, fish, reptiles, birds and mammals, as well as on sperm and eggs of several species. In point of years, Spallanzani was preceded by Reaumur who, in about 1740, in addition to inventing a temperature scale (as noted in Chapter 5) made studies of the effect of cold on insects. Other early investigators included Henry Power who, during the decade 1660-1670, froze a jar of vinegar eels in an ice-salt mixture and found they were active as ever after they were thawed. He concluded from this that cold, unlike heat, did not possess a killing property. In 1683, Robert Boyle froze frogs and fishes, but not all survived (especially after prolonged freezing) and he concluded that cold, as well as heat, could kill. However, Spallanzani was the first to make extensive studies; then Father B. J. Luyet of St. Louis University a century and a half later was the first to establish a systematic basis for studies in cryobiology. His book, "Life and Death at Low Temperatures," published in 1940, laid the foundations for further research in this area.

Certain fundamental concepts relating life and temperature have emerged. One interesting fact is that man can tolerate only a very small increase above normal temperatures before death occurs, whereas he can experience much greater decreases below normal temperature and survive (See Figure 12-1).

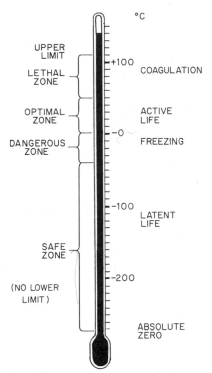

FIG. 12-1   The temperature on vital processes.

It can be shown that freezing in itself does not cause death but that the associated effects can kill. These effects include mechanical injury due directly to crystal formation, and "chemical" injury from the increased concentration of salts and other dissolved substances in the remaining fluid.

It has also been found that these associated undesirable effects can be minimized by the use of additives and by control of cooling rates. Thus there is a critical temperature at about —130°C (—202°F), above which ice crystal growth can occur. Below —130°C all chemical and physical activity is reduced to a negligible level and recovery after storage is more likely. This safe zone is lower than one would infer from the danger zone of 0 to 50°C indicated on Luyet's thermometer in Figure 12-1.

Cooling rates are often characterized as "fast" or "slow." A process in which a biological specimen is cooled at the rate of several hundred degrees Centigrade per minute is called "fast." On the other hand, "slow" cooling proceeds at rates from 1° to 20°C per minute.

Fast freezing provides the key to high cell recoveries essential for freezing blood that is to be used for transfusions. A pint of blood can be frozen uniformly in 40 seconds in a container immersed in liquid nitrogen, at the rate of 350°C per minute. Slow freezing, on the other hand, is desired for sperm and most mammalian tissues that are to be preserved by freezing. In slow freezing precise control is essential, because quite different results are obtained for a change in rate of cooling of a material from 1°C per minute to 5°C per minute. To obtain the desired results, it may be necessary to modify the cooling technique, or to increase the rate of cooling at one or more points in the cooling cycle. While remarkable results can be obtained in low-temperature preservation of biological materials, the method requires painstaking analysis and development for each and every biological material. An apparatus for freezing biological specimens at a controlled rate is shown in Figure 12-2.

As one example of the complexity of freezing (and thawing) rates, tissues from rabbit ears died when frozen quickly and thawed quickly, or when frozen quickly and thawed slowly. They survived only when frozen slowly and thawed quickly.

One interesting example in nature of the use of anti-freeze additives to permit the safe freezing of living organisms is the production each autumn by fish of substances which reduce the freezing points of their blood and tissue fluids.

An alternative technique to preservation by freezing and cold storage is freeze-drying, whereby the water is removed from the frozen material by vacuum sublimation of the ice at low temperatures to give a dry product which can be stored at normal temperatures and rehydrated prior to use. From the theoretical point of view, cells which survive separation from their other constituents of their water content in the form of ice at low temperatures should not be harmed if the ice were then removed by

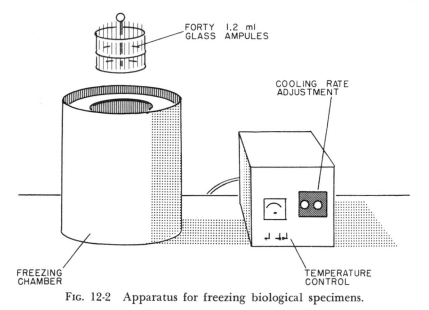

FORTY 1.2 ml
GLASS AMPULES

COOLING RATE
ADJUSTMENT

FREEZING
CHAMBER

TEMPERATURE
CONTROL

FIG. 12-2 Apparatus for freezing biological specimens.

sublimation-drying. As a practical matter, however, the drying temperature may well lie in the critical zone (0 to 50°C) where damage to the specimen is likely. Therefore, although the prospect of simpler and more economic storage of freeze-dried material at room temperature is attractive, the fact remains that materials of value in research or medicine are better stored at liquid nitrogen temperatures where there is no hazard of damage in drying and where the period of safe storage is essentially unlimited.

In freeze drying, of course, the freezing itself may be effected either by use of a cryogenic fluid, such as liquid nitrogen, or by mechanical refrigeration.

IN SEMEN PRESERVATION

Artificial insemination has long been practiced on horses, dogs and sheep: in fact it was used by the Arabs as early as the 14th century. The widespread use of artificial insemination for the breeding of farm animals was first developed by Russian workers in the early 1920's. The first artificial insemination program for the improvement of dairy cattle was organized by a cooperative organization in New Jersey in May of 1938. Twenty years later, in 1958, more than 33% of the dairy cattle population in the United States was artificially inseminated. In those 20 years, the industry expanded 900%. Except for hybrid corn, no other agricultural product can match this growth rate.

The artificial insemination of livestock has grown in this rapid fashion because it offers a number of real advantages.

1. The number of cows mated with one bull has been increased from an average of 25 - 50 before artificial insemination to about 2500. (One technique that has aided this expansion is the dilution of fresh semen.) Waste has been reduced, and artificial insemination has been made possible, even on an international scale.
2. Selective breeding is possible, since superior bulls may be utilized to a greater extent than under natural conditions.
3. The cost of keeping bulls is eliminated; the cost of maintaining of a single bull will pay breeding fees for 20 - 40 cows.
4. The dangers of keeping bulls are avoided. On average, one person is killed every four days by bulls on the farms of the United States.
5. Diseases, such as venereal diseases, which were spread by natural mating, can now be controlled. Furthermore, during epidemics of infections such as foot and mouth disease, a reserve of frozen semen can be used until danger of further contagion has passed.
6. Older sires can be bred with young cows which have not had calves (heifers) without damage to these cows.
7. Improvement of breeding stock can be effected by restricting the use of semen from selected bulls to produce only a limited number of progeny until they had been tested for milk yield and other qualities.

Refrigerated sperm storage was first used in 1952. It permitted safe transportation, and preservation for indefinite periods. The initial application followed the scientific breakthrough in England in 1949 by Polge, Smith and Parkes, who discovered that fowl semen could be frozen and revived by thawing.

Today the preservation of bull semen is almost entirely a cryogenic operation. Solid carbon dioxide (Dry Ice) may be used as the refrigerant but the —79°C (—110°F) temperature of a solid carbon dioxide-alcohol mixture is perilously close to a critical temperature of —65°C (—85°F), above which there is a high loss in storage. At liquid nitrogen temperatures, the stability is excellent; the storage of bull semen at liquid nitrogen temperatures is a standard practice and, in fact, consumes about 6 tons of liquid nitrogen per day in the United States. Figure 12-3

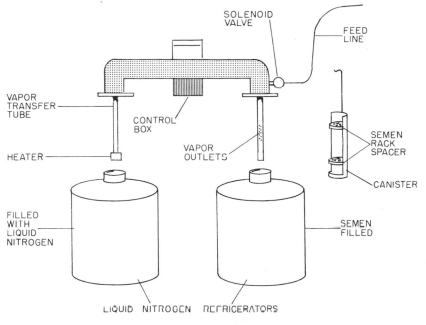

FIG. 12-3   Bovine semen freezer.

shows a typical bovine semen freezer, and Figure 12-4 shows the consequences of using cryogenic techniques in conjunction with artificial insemination.

Another possibility, not yet commercially exploited, involves the transplantation of eggs or ova from a superior cow to an

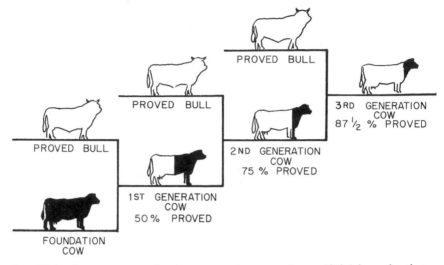

FIG. 12-4 Consequences of using cryogenic means for artificial insemination.

inferior cow for incubation. Thus, a superior cow might be able to transmit her hereditary qualities to many more than the ten or so calves than it is now possible for her to produce in a normal lifetime.

While bovine semen has been the easiest and most important application of refrigerated storage techniques, there are a number of other attractive posssibilities in commercial breeding, where, however, problems remain to be solved. Hog semen is next in importance economically, but difficulties have been encountered both in preservation and in insemination technique. Research is continuing, however, and is yielding some promising results.

Today, of the 19 million dairy cattle in the United States, 7.5 million are being artificially inseminated, 4.5 million of them with semen from cryogenic storage. On the other hand, there are 27 million beef cattle of which only 0.5 million are artificially inseminated, only half of those by semen from cryogenic storage. Premium beef requirements may cause the beef industry to become the next major expansion area for the use of frozen semen.

Still another possibility is the preservation of human sperm by freezing. This plan could be used in the creation of radiation-shielded banks of human sperms to assure the survival of humanity in the event of large-scale atomic warfare. It could also be used in the selective breeding of humans of superior intellectual and physical ability. A two-year study at the University of Arkansas School of Medicine, involving over a hundred people, has shown that human semen can be frozen, stored, thawed and used to produce normal children.

As far back as 1866, the fact that human spermatazoa would survive freezing at —17°C was reported by Mantegazza, in Italy. He suggested that men killed on the battlefield could become, posthumously, the fathers of legitimate offspring. He was the first to predict the use of cold in methods for artificial insemination of humans (and animals). However, he was ahead of his time and temperatures low enough to arrest biochemical change were not available until about 1900, as has been explained in Chapters 1 and 3.

The application of cryogenic techniques to semen preservation provides the first system for putting desirable genetic characteristics on file — even for centuries. It may also permit the preservation of economically important wild species, such as salmon. One day it may even lead to the elucidation of the biochemical reasons for a George Bernard Shaw or an Adolf Hitler. It certainly has great potential for the future.

IN BLOOD PRESERVATION

The preservation of whole human blood for transfusions for long periods has been a major problem since World War I. Present-day procedures involve storage at 4°C in the presence of an anticoagulant; unfortunately, under these conditions whole blood may be stored only for 21 days. After that period, the blood is unsuitable for transfusion, because of hemolysis (the rupture of red cells). This time limitation of storage is a serious handicap to the maintenance of adequate blood banks, both because of the losses of outdated supplies and also because of seasonal fluctuations in blood donation.

Two new techniques are now being developed under the

sponsorship of the Office of Naval Research of the United States Navy, which has been supporting such work since 1955.

The first of these techniques is the separation from blood of the red cells, addition to them of glycerol, freezing, and storage at —80°C (—112°F). When blood is needed, the cells are thawed, the glycerol removed, and the cells re-suspended in a plasma. The equipment required is relatively complex, so that this method should be best adapted to central hospitals and other large institutions.

The second of these techniques would be ideal for military field hospitals, although it could also be used in central hospitals. It involves ultra-rapid freezing (in one minute or less) at —196°C (—321°F) of whole blood. Polyvinyl pyrrolidone (PVP) is used as a protective additive. Unlike glycerol, it need not be removed before use. In fact it was used extensively as a blood plasma extender, by the Germans in World War II. When needed, the blood is thawed as rapidly as it was frozen.

Figure 12-5 shows a container which has been developed to

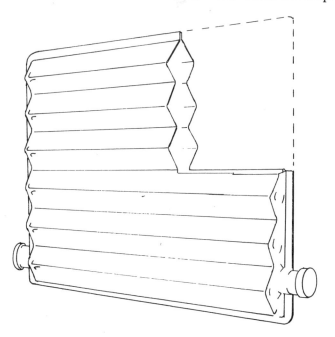

FIG. 12-5   Special container for blood to permit rapid freezing.

permit rapid freezing and thawing. It is designed so that the blood within it is distributed in layers of uniform thickness at all points to assure even freezing. Figure 12-6 shows a liquid nitrogen refrigerator for storage and transports of blood and other biological materials.

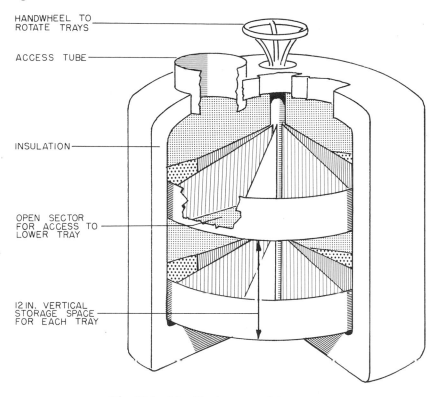

HANDWHEEL TO
ROTATE TRAYS

ACCESS TUBE

INSULATION

OPEN SECTOR
FOR ACCESS TO
LOWER TRAY

12 IN. VERTICAL
STORAGE SPACE
FOR EACH TRAY

FIG. 12-6   Liquid nitrogen refrigerator.

Blood preservation is a big business. Over 6 million pints of blood are now used annually in transfusions; this figure is expected to rise to 8.5 million pints by 1970. At a price of about $25 per pint, the dollar volume is huge. Perhaps even more significant is the value to the country for use in the event of military and civilian disasters. Cryogenic techniques seem to offer a major step forward in this vital area.

IN BONE MARROW PRESERVATION

The successful transfusion of bone marrow in human patients may soon become a practical reality, due to applications of cryogenics. The same type of quick-freezing methods which have proved successful with blood are now being tested for application to bone marrow.

The physiological function of bone marrow is to form blood cells. When bone marrow is destroyed by radiation or by chemotherapy, it no longer produces the required blood cells. Therefore marrow transfusions would be very desirable for the treatment of patients so affected, and are undergoing extensive research. This work is not concerned so much with cryogenic storage, which is well developed, as it is with immunological compatibility and other biochemical matters. It is to be hoped that processing centers and central repositories for frozen bone marrow will be available in the future.

IN TISSUE CULTURE PRESERVATION

Low-temperature preservation of tissues and cells provides an excellent source of reference specimens, which are especially valuable for long-term experiments. In addition, transport under low-temperature conditions permits samples of the same reference material to be distributed to investigators in different locations, enabling them to run comparison experiments. For example, the study of tumorous growths should be greatly assisted by this application of cryogenics.

Prior to the development of low-temperature preservation techniques, tissue and cell cultures have been maintained by subculturing, a procedure in which samples are re-grown once or twice a week. This procedure is time-consuming and costly, and it introduces a number of experimental hazards, such as those of chromosomal mutations; contamination of the culture with bacteria, viruses, or other foreign organisms; and accidental loss of the culture through frequent handling. All of these hazards are eliminated by low-temperature preservation. It requires, as does the preservation of blood and other biological materials, freezing at controlled rates and the use of preservative additives.

Another tissue which has been the subject of many preservation studies is the cornea of the eye. Considerable success has been achieved in transplanting corneal tissues from cadavers to individuals whose corneas have been scarred or otherwise damaged. Sophisticated freeze-drying techniques have been successfully applied to corneal tissue grafts in both animals and man. The use of glycerol as a preservative in freezing and frozen storage is somewhat simpler than in the case of blood, and has found wider application in banking corneal tissue.

IN ANIMAL GLAND PRESERVATION

The preservation of animal glands by cryogenic means may be of immediate interest in the preparation of polio vaccines because it would permit importation of monkey glands rather than entire monkeys from Africa, to provide the growth medium for the vaccine.

Animal gland freezing, preservation, thawing, and reimplantation by surgery offers the most impressive possibility of establishing banks of human organs in which spare body parts could be stored for later transplantation to people with defective organs. As in the case of bone marrow, there is of course the immunological problem which must be met and conquered. Effective methods of animal gland preservation would also facilitate the transport and storage of glands to be processed to recover active ingredients, such as insulin, ACTH, and other therapeutic substances.

IN SEED AND POLLEN PRESERVATION

Brown and Escombe, working in Dewar's laboratory in 1897, were among the first to study the biological effects of low temperatures. They found that the germinative power of seeds was not affected by slow cooling to liquid air temperatures and storage at —190°C (—310°F) for 11 hours. Similar results were obtained at liquid hydrogen temperatures by other workers.

In this application the economics of freezing preservation are not favorable and freeze drying is probably more suitable.

IN MICROORGANISM PRESERVATION

As early as 1900, when liquid air had been available in quantity for only 5 years and when liquid hydrogen had been known for only 2 years, studies were made on their effects on bacteria and on enzymes. McFayden and Rowland, working in Dewar's laboratory, reported that these materials were unimpaired in vitality and activity after exposure to or storage in these cryogenic fluids.

Cold has surprisingly little effect on microorganisms; certain species have actually multiplied while held at a temperature of —9° (—16°F) for a year. Bacteria frozen in the Antarctic ice for half a century have recently been found alive; the organisms were recovered from human excrement at the camp sites of the Scott and Shackleton expeditions, which date from the early 1900's.

The use of liquid nitrogen temperatures to preserve microorganisms may make it possible to store indefinitely types which are difficult to preserve even for short periods by other techniques. This technique may facilitate the diagnosis of diseases due to yeasts and fungi, such as infections of the lymph nodes.

In industry, cryogenic preservation of antibiotic standards and microorganisms for assay work promises to be of great value. Even more valuable is the potential application of cryogenic storage to the preservation of valuable strains of yeast or bacteria without change for long periods of time. Such materials are widely used in industrial fermentations, so that maintenance of the original stock culture without genetic change is obviously important to the successful continuation of a process. Storage at liquid nitrogen temperatures makes such preservation possible and practical.

Bacterial suspensions tolerate rapid freezing without the use of protective additives. A stream of droplets of a bacterial suspension can thus be frozen simply by directing a jet of the material from an ordinary syringe into liquid nitrogen. The droplets must be small in size to assure rapid freezing, so that they float for about a second in the liquid nitrogen and then freeze and sink. When a sample is to be recovered, a spoon cooled by liquid nitrogen is used to sprinkle the droplets into a warm, saline bath; or else they may be placed in a small container and warmed in a water bath, thus avoiding dilution. One hundred per cent survival of bacteria has been shown by plate counts after this freeze-thaw treatment.

IN ENZYME PRESERVATION

Enzymatic reactions do not cease below the freezing point of water, but merely proceed more slowly. Thus the lipases, which hydrolyze fats, are still active at —24.5°C (—12°F); trypsin, which hydolyzes proteins, is active at —15°C (5°F) and invertase can hydrolyze sucrose at —18°C. (0°F). However, repeated freezing and thawing commonly leads to almost complete loss of enzymatic activity.

The technique described above for microorganisms — that of freezing droplets by spraying them directly into liquid nitrogen without the addition of preservatives, can also be applied to enzyme extracts.

IN TREATMENT OF SKIN DISEASES

Liquid nitrogen may be used in the treatment of warts and of scarring caused by acne. It is applied by an ordinary cotton swab; when the lesion is touched, freezing occurs almost instantly. Contact time may be 10 to 60 seconds, the aim being to initiate the formation of a blister just sufficient to separate the wart from the surrounding tissues. The blister appears 6 to 8 hours after treatment, exfoliation of the undesired area occurs, and the final cosmetic result is good.

IN CRYOSURGERY

Cryosurgery, the application of cold to surgical techniques, has two major applications. It is used in producing anaesthesia by lowering of body temperature, and it is used in neurosurgery to apply liquid nitrogen temperatures, with pin-point accuracy, to very small areas of the brain.

In cold anesthesia, lowering the body temperature retards the entire metabolic process. The patient's oxygen requirements are cut by 50%. Circulation slows down and bleeding becomes much more controlled, which makes the surgeon's work easier. When the deep body temperature of man is reduced to between 20 to 30°C (68 to 86°F), the oxygen requirements of the organs and tissues are reduced so greatly that circulation of blood by the heart can cease for as long as about 8 minutes without causing damage to the brain and other vital organs by stopping their supply of oxygenated blood. Surgical operations can then be performed on the heart under relatively bloodless conditions. Cold deadens pain in a pleasant way, with no unpleasant taste or nausea as after-effects. The strain on the heart and on other vital organs is reduced, thus increasing chances of recovery and diminishing the possibility of post-operative shock.

Bloodless brain surgery with real hope of alleviating Parkinson's disease ("shaking palsy" — a disease of the central nervous system which causes tremors of the extremities) is another contribution of cryogenics. A needle-like device called a cannula is inserted into the thalamus (a mass of gray matter at the base of the brain which controls the transmission of nerve impulses) while the patient is under a local anesthetic. Rapid X-rays using Polaroid film are used to check the course of the cannula. As this needle is moved about, liquid nitrogen is passed through an inner tube within it, chilling its tip to about —10°C (14°F) (See Figure 12-7). Temporary freezing of the section of the brain around the tip occurs, and when the section frozen is that which causes the tremor of the patient's extremities, the shaking stops. In this way the region of the brain that controls the shaking

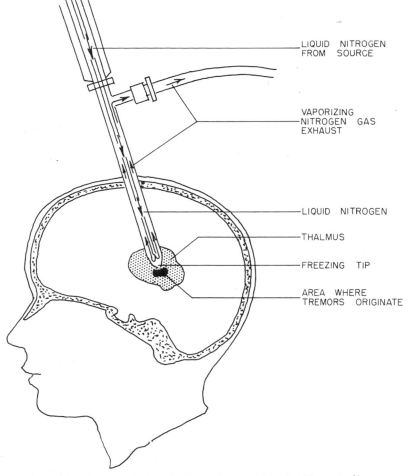

LIQUID NITROGEN
FROM SOURCE

VAPORIZING
NITROGEN GAS
EXHAUST

LIQUID NITROGEN

THALMUS

FREEZING TIP

AREA WHERE
TREMORS ORIGINATE

FIG. 12-7 Cryosurgical technique for treating Parkinson's disease.

can be located and destroyed by prolonged freezing (perhaps 3 minutes at —40°C (—40°F)). The exploration does no damage to the other parts of the brain, since they thaw normally if frozen for 30 seconds or less.

The application of cryosurgical techniques to the destruction of tumors in the brain and elsewhere in the body is now the subject of research.

Chapter 13

HOW COLD IS USED
— IN FOOD HANDLING

The average United States citizen consumes over 1,000 pounds of food per year. Of this amount, about 5% is handled as frozen food, 30% is handled without freezing under a lesser degree of refrigeration, and perhaps 1% is handled at room temperature but is protected from adverse environmental effects by shipment in an inert atmosphere (See Figure 13-1). Each of these categories represents an application of cryogenics — the first two use liquid nitrogen as a refrigerant, while the third belongs in the cryogenic group because the gaseous nitrogen required has, like liquid nitrogen, been separated from the air by cryogenic means.

Freezing as a means of preservation of foodstuffs dates back to a patent granted in 1842 to H. Benjamin in England for freezing food by immersion in ice and salt brine. By 1880 mechanical refrigeration was used for a cargo of frozen meat shipped from Australia to Great Britain. The major expansion came in 1929 after the development of quick freezing methods and of small containers suitable for frozen-food handling in retail trade. By 1935 a billion pounds of frozen food were handled in the United States alone; by 1944 the figure had grown to 3 billion pounds; and it now approximates 10 billion pounds.

The dimensions of the volume of food handled under refrigeration in the United States alone can be judged from 1959 statistics. In that year 8 billion pounds of frozen food and 67 billion pounds

ABOUT 200 BILLION POUNDS OF FOOD ARE CONSUMED EACH YEAR IN THE U.S.A.

OF WHICH —

67 BILLION POUNDS ARE SHIPPED REFRIGERATED

AND

8 BILLION FROZEN

SHIPPING

FROZEN AND REFRIGERATED
FOOD REQUIRES:

115,000 RAILWAY CARS

200,000 TRUCKS

40,000 TRAILERS

Fig. 13-1 Comparative quantities of total refrigerated and frozen foods processed in U. S.

of perishable food were sold. The transport of this food required 115,000 railroad cars, 40,000 highway trailers, and 200,000 long- and short-haul trucks. Considering the frozen food alone and assuming that 2 cubic feet of nitrogen would be required per pound of food transported from freezing plant to distributing warehouse, one can foresee a nitrogen demand of 16 billion cubic feet per year or somewhat better than a billion pounds per year. Transport from the distributing warehouse to the retail marketer would increase this potential further. The use of liquid nitrogen for refrigeration of the fresh meat and produce which are shipped at 35°F (2°C) would further increase these figures.

IN FOOD FREEZING

The freezing of foods by liquid nitrogen is an attractive possibility, but not a new one. Clarence Birdseye, the frozen food pioneer, reportedly tried it about 1925 but abandoned it because of the cost. The advent of cheaper nitrogen and vastly improved insulation techniques are now leading to a re-examination of the commercial capabilities of this process. The freezing of foods by immersion in liquid nitrogen is primarily of interest for products that cannot be frozen satisfactorily by other methods.

The immersion freezing of citrus fruits gives a hard product which shatters like the the rubber ball in the traditional demonstration of the properties of liquid air. The frozen fruit can be crushed to give individual citrus cells that can be shipped in the frozen state; such cells could be used as flavoring agents in confectionary products or in cottage cheese.

Tomatoes and bananas have been frozen by immersion in liquid nitrogen and the products obtained are reported to retain many of the qualities of the fresh variety. An ear of corn frozen in this way can be divested of its kernels with no loss in vitamin content, flavor or kernel size. Strawberries and meat have been studied for the effect of immersion freezing in nitrogen, and even pastry and bakery goods have been frozen commercially in this medium.

An apparatus for immersion freezing of foodstuffs in liquid nitrogen is shown in Figure 13-2. It is a conveyor consisting of slats carried by two parallel chains. Figure 13-3 shows another design, an elevator-style freezer which can be installed outdoors adjacent to cold storage and food processing rooms. Such devices have been applied to the freezing of chicken pot pie, ham, and other cooked foods. First contact with the liquid nitrogen freezes all exposed surfaces, sealing in flavor and aroma. The process takes seven minutes as compared to the 3 to 48 minutes needed to freeze food by some other methods.

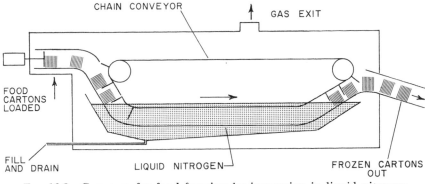

FIG. 13-2   Conveyor for food freezing by immersion in liquid nitrogen.

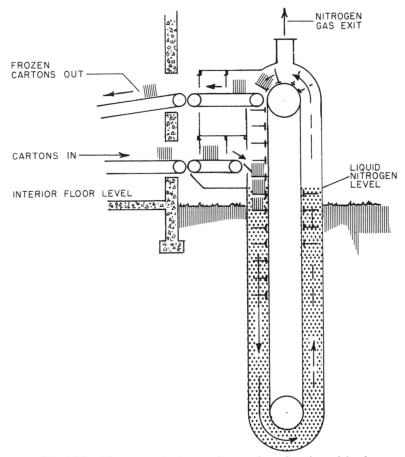

FIG. 13-3   Elevator style freezer for outdoor freezing of foods.

IN REFRIGERATED FOOD SHIPMENT

The combination of the low boiling point — 196°C (—320°F) and the high heat of vaporization (86 Btu/lb) of liquid nitrogen, plus the fact that the gas absorbs about 80 Btu per pound in going from its boiling point to 0°F, make liquid nitrogen an attractive refrigerant. A further advantage is the fact that nitrogen expands 600-fold in its transformation from a liquid to a gas, this cold gas constituting an effective medium for cooling all parts of an enclosure.

Temperatures of —100°F (—73°C) are always most economically attained using liquid nitrogen. At 0 - 32°F (—18 - 0°C), the economics of nitrogen are less favorable and liquid nitrogen cannot compete on a cost basis alone with, for example, a refrigerator using an electric motor drive. Refrigerators which are operated by internal combustion engines, as are the refrigerators on transport vehicles, are more expensive to operate, however, and nitrogen refrigeration can compete effectively with them.

Liquifreeze Process

In the Liquifreeze process, developed by Willard Morrison, liquid nitrogen is used to freeze the water content of the food; one then relies on this ice and the evaporation of the liquid nitrogen remaining in the insulated container to maintain food temperature at the required low level during shipment. In a six-week trip from California to New York via the Panama Canal, a mixed load of frozen food prepared by the Liquifreeze process arrived at its destination at a temperature of — 37°C (—34°F).

In this process, liquid nitrogen is pumped into an insulated box packed with frozen food. As the liquid nitrogen vaporizes and escapes through vent holes in the box, the temperature drops to as low as —129°C (—200°F). The temperature remains below zero for as long as a month—quite adequate for 10-day cross-country rail trips and for longer ocean voyages.

The Polarstream Method

In the Polarstream method, liquid nitrogen is stored aboard a truck or railroad car used to transport frozen foods. When the temperature falls to a predetermined level, a thermostat opens a valve on the liquid container and releases a stream of nitrogen droplets and cold vapor through a manifold, located at the top of the refrigerated space, which is similar to a fire sprinkler manifold. The cooling of the cargo space is rapid and effective. A multistop delivery truck equipped with a Polarstream installation is shown in Figure 13-4.

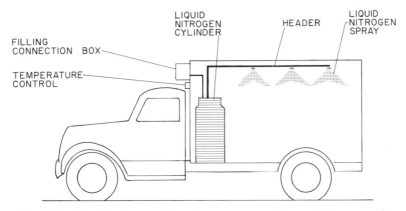

FIG. 13-4   Liquid nitrogen installation in a multistop delivery truck.

The Polarstream method is also being applied to piggy-back trailers and to railroad freight cars (See Figure 13-5). The nitrogen-refrigerated rail car may be compared with Figure 13-6, which shows an older car using ice for cooling. The ultimate in Polarstream application may well be nitrogen-refrigerated trucks powered by gas turbine engines and able to draw on nitrogen filling stations the country over (See Figure 13-7).

The use of liquid nitrogen as a refrigerant for vehicles affords a very versatile system, one which can be used to transport perishables at $+55°F$ ($13°C$) on one trip and ice cream at $—20°F$ ($—29°C$) on another. For refrigeration of ice cream, liquid nitrogen is effectively not only for the short hauls and frequent

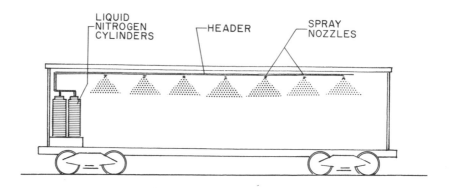

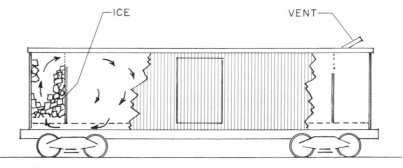

FIG. 13-5   (*above*) Freight car refrigerated by liquid nitrogen.
FIG. 13-6   (*below*) Freight car refrigerated by ice.

stops of retail service, but also for long distance hauling. The future may see greater centralization of the ice cream industry in a smaller number of large plants with liquid nitrogen playing a major part in the distribution of quality products from these plants.

Some physical advantages claimed for liquid nitrogen cooling as opposed to mechanical refrigeration include (1) less precooling time, nitrogen can cool a truck to 0°F (—18°C) in less than 5 minutes; (2) simplicity, the only moving part is the control valve in the line from the nitrogen cylinder to the spray header; (3) ease of automatic control, single-valve control combined with high cooling power to permit good control even in hot weather with frequent door openings; (4) moisture retention by cargo, the forced

Fig. 13-7 Tomorrow's refrigerated truck stop supplying turbine fuel and liquid nitrogen.

convection that accompanies mechanical refrigeration can cause 1 to 2% loss in weight of a meat cargo en route to the recipient.

These advantages may be counterbalanced by somewhat higher operating costs, particularly when small fleets of 10 trucks or less are involved. The only other negative factor is the possibility of producing an atmosphere so rich in nitrogen that it is not safe to breathe. However, the displacement of cold nitrogen by warm air is usually so rapid that the driver can enter the insulated cargo compartment as soon as the doors have been opened, the nitrogen valve being closed by an interlock when the doors are open.

IN FOOD HANDLING UNDER INERT ATMOSPHERES

A number of foodstuffs are now being processed and shipped under a nitrogen atmosphere. This procedure has the advantage in processing of preventing loss from rodents, bacteria, or fire. It has the consumer-appeal of preserving flavor and aroma, and preventing spoilage.

Food processing applications of nitrogen atmospheres include the whipping of margarine and butter, the powdering of potatoes, and the grinding of coffee. In bulk storage, nitrogen atmospheres are used for alfalfa, wheat, and flour, as well as the cold storage of apples, where they have been found to lengthen storage life greatly.

In shipping, powdered potatoes, ground coffee, peanuts and other products containing oxidizable oils are protected by nitrogen gas. Still another application is the bulk shipment of wine and citrus fruit juices.

Chapter 14

HOW COLD IS USED
—IN ELECTRONICS

Inherent in any electrical circuit are random voltage fluctuations which are a function of the operating temperature of the circuit. By operating at liquid helium temperatures instead of room temperatures, this "noise" can be decreased by a factor of 100, and the efficiency of the circuit can be greatly enhanced.

Cryogenic electronics — or cryotronics as it is sometimes called — is concerned not only with this improved performance from low temperature operation, but also with phenomena which occur only at low temperatures. These unique low temperature phenomena are treated in the following chapter, which deals with the application of low temperatures in superconductive devices, this present chapter being devoted to electronic devices which operate more efficiently under cryogenic conditions.

IN MASERS

Microwave amplification by stimulated emission of radiation has given rise to the acronym "maser." Masers are devices which utilize transitions between energy states of a molecule or atom for amplification of microwave energy. They operate by exciting certain internal energy states higher than the normal or "ground" state, so that the atom or molecule, upon receipt of a signal of the correct frequency, is stimulated to radiate energy in phase

157

with the signal and so amplify the signal. Since the energy which can be imparted by one molecule is so small, the energies of large numbers of molecules must be tapped to obtain usable amounts of power. They may be in any state of aggregation; one widely-used form is a crystal, which has the atoms that are to be excited dispersed through it. One such crystal is the ruby, which contains trivalent chromium ions dispersed in a matrix of alumina. Synthetic ruby is used in preference to natural ruby because it can be obtained at lower cost in controlled composition and shape.

Low temperature operation of maser crystals is necessary so that thermal vibrations of the atoms do not interfere with the adsorption-emission of microwave energy. At low temperatures the difference in population of atoms between two energy levels, which is the basis of maser action, is greater. Thus masers work best at liquid helium temperatures but can operate with reduced efficiency at temperatures of liquid nitrogen.

The theoretical conception of the maser was proposed in 1952 by Dr. Charles H. Townes, who was then at Columbia University and is now Provost at Massachusetts Institute of Technology. Townes also predicted, together with A. L. Schawlow of Bell Telephone Laboratories, the optical maser (or laser) from theoretical considerations in 1958.

The construction of a typical maser is shown in Figure 14-1. It is called a three-level maser from the fact that it uses three of the four available energy levels in the chromium ions in a ruby crystal. The signal is fed in at the top and passes down a waveguide into the ruby crystal, which is located in a dewar between the poles of a magnet. The magnetic field contains a resonant cavity which increases the field strength in the active material and has an effect equivalent to passing the radiation many times through the ruby; it splits the energy levels of the atom. The signal is reflected and returns up the waveguide. The incoming and outgoing signals are separated in an isolator. The pump power is fed through a second waveguide.

The value of the maser is its low noise level as compared with a conventional microwave amplifier. Noise is commonly expressed by electronic engineers in terms of equivalent absolute temperature values. Thus, a conventional microwave amplifier may have a noise level of 2100°K, of which 300°K is contributed

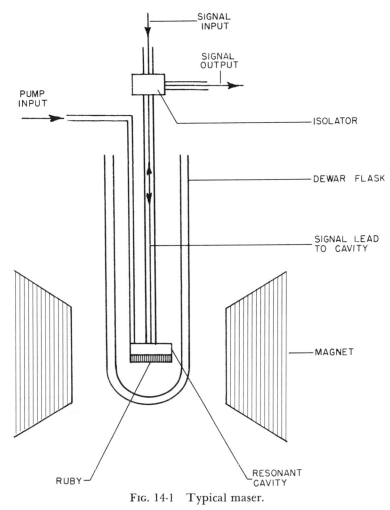

FIG. 14-1 Typical maser.

by the input load and 1800°K by the receiver itself. A maser receiver, on the other hand, could have a noise level of 3°K. The input need not be cooled, however, if one looks above the horizon into the sky, which has an apparent noise temperature of only about 2.5°K. Thus the total noise level is the 2.5°K of the input, plus perhaps 4.5°K for the aerial and feeder, plus perhaps 3°K for the maser receiver or 10°K in all. This is about one per cent of the noise level of a conventional microwave receiver.

Masers form the heart of radiotelescopes which receive signals from objects many millions of light years more distant in space than those visible in the best optical telescopes. Radioastronomy demands very low noise levels in amplifiers because the signals are so weak.

It has also been suggested that maser radar devices may allow a few ground stations to control the air space over the whole United States, while airborne instruments will give much better range detection capability than has heretofore been possible.

Communications satellites, inaugurated by the pioneer Echo project and carried a step nearer everyday use by Project Telstar, depend on cryogenically cooled masers for reception of the reflected signal from space. (See Figure 14-2.)

The heart of Telstar is the maser which receives the signal from the orbiting satellite and translates it back into an intelligible message. It is shown in Figure 14-3. The remote location and the necessity for dependable, uninterrupted operation of

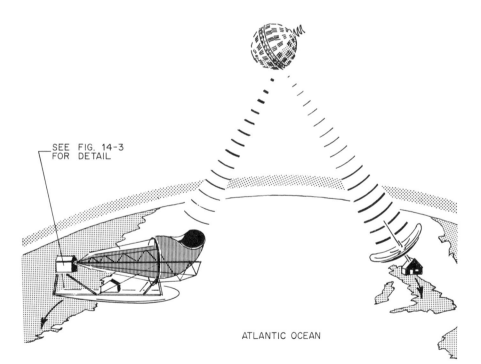

SEE FIG. 14-3
FOR DETAIL

ATLANTIC OCEAN

FIG. 14-2   Cryogenics and Telstar—overall schematic.

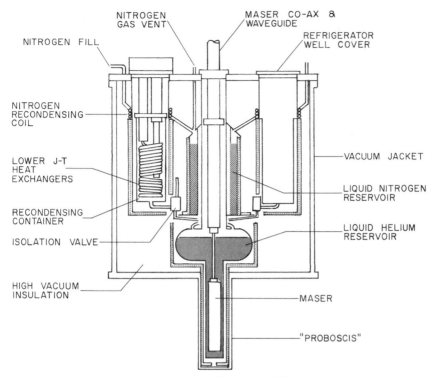

NITROGEN
GAS VENT

MASER CO-AX &
WAVEGUIDE

NITROGEN FILL

REFRIGERATOR
WELL COVER

NITROGEN
RECONDENSING
COIL

LOWER J-T
HEAT
EXCHANGERS

RECONDENSING
CONTAINER

ISOLATION VALVE

HIGH VACUUM
INSULATION

VACUUM JACKET

LIQUID NITROGEN
RESERVOIR

LIQUID HELIUM
RESERVOIR

MASER

"PROBOSCIS"

FIG. 14-3   The cold heart of Telstar.

the ground receiving station made necessary the development of
a compact, continuous, closed-cycle device of the type shown for
the supply of refrigeration in the fractional wattage range at or
near the temperature of liquid helium (4°K). Continuous operation requires equipment having a service life of at least 10,000
hours, and unattended continuous operating periods of 2,000
hours or more between shutdowns for routine maintenance. Two
completely independent refrigeration systems were provided,
either of which would have adequate capacity to cool the maser
and maintain the equipment at operating temperatures; these
are shown in Figure 14-3.

IN LASERS

The application of the maser principle to light rather than microwaves has resulted in light amplification by stimulated emission of radiation — in the laser or optical maser.

Unfortunately spontaneous emission is more likely than stimulated emission in the optical region of the spectrum. However, such stimulated emission as is produced is phase-coherent, which means that the beam produced is very intense, even though the probability of the production of energy quanta by individual atoms is not great.

The conditions for laser action are that an emissive condition must be established and then that the optical arrangement must be such that a large number of atoms radiate in phase. The first condition is realized by discharging a bank of condensers through a high intensity flash tube, thus raising chromium ions in ruby to an excited state. When they fall to the ground state they emit their characteristic red fluorescence, which is in a narrow spectral band. The second condition is realized by silvering optical flats on either end of a ruby crystal, one heavily and one lightly. The phase-coherent beam issues through the lightly silvered end as shown in Figure 14-4.

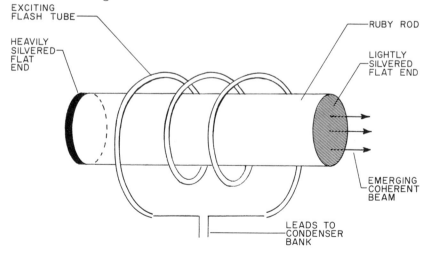

Fig. 14-4   The fundamentals of laser action.

It is to be noted that ruby crystals may be used as the active material in the laser, as well as in the maser. The fundamental action is different because the laser uses the directly excited energy levels of the chromium ion while the maser operates on magnetically split levels. There are, of course, many materials other than ruby which can be used for lasers, some which may even be superior, particularly from the standpoint of power requirements, which are very high in the case of ruby. Samarium or uranium ions in a calcium fluoride matrix show promise as laser materials requiring less pumping power. Whereas ruby lasers can only function in pulsed operation due to the high power requirements, it is hoped that newer materials will permit continuous operation.

Figure 14-5 shows a laboratory device for investigating materials for laser action. This device permits low temperature operation, which is important since laser action varies widely with temperature. In fact, some crystals which do not work at all at room temperature, exhibit laser action when cooled. Even those crystals that do work at room temperature yield a much greater output at cryogenic temperatures.

The many applications of lasers that have been proposed include their use:

1. As light sources for photochemical reactions
2. As light sources for battlefield illumination
3. As heat sources for welding and cutting of metals
4. In communications systems for space
5. In missile tracking and destruction
6. In noise-free, interception proof, telephone systems
7. In light detection and ranging systems similar to radar
8. In undersea detection and ranging systems similar to sonar
9. In medicine and biology for such applications as the welding of the retina in eye repair operations

Some of the more immediate possibilities are discussed in the following paragraphs. Even these applications require other tech-

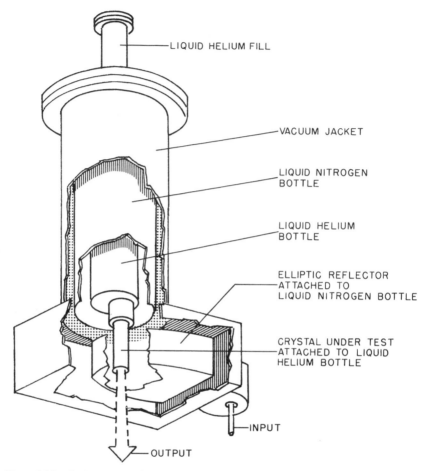

LIQUID HELIUM FILL

VACUUM JACKET

LIQUID NITROGEN BOTTLE

LIQUID HELIUM BOTTLE

ELLIPTIC REFLECTOR ATTACHED TO LIQUID NITROGEN BOTTLE

CRYSTAL UNDER TEST ATTACHED TO LIQUID HELIUM BOTTLE

INPUT

OUTPUT

FIG. 14-5 Laboratory device for study of laser materials at cryogenic temperatures.

nological developments if they are to be reduced to practice, one of which is an optical transmission cable to conduct laser beams in a closed system. Other applications require the development of new types of lasers, which will operate in other colors than ruby red. A blue-green laser is needed for maximum transmission efficiency through sea water in a sonar type system.

Optical frequencies have a number of advantages over radio frequencies for use in communications systems. At the higher optical frequencies, a larger band width becomes available and more information can be carried. The high carrier frequency of optical signals means that narrow beams can be transmitted without the use of large antennas. A microwave antenna 1,000 feet in diameter would be needed to produce a beam as concentrated as that from a $\frac{1}{4}$ inch ruby maser.

A possible laser communications system is shown in Figure 14-6. Audio signals modulate the light emerging from the laser oscillator. The modulated light travels through space to a receiver, which has its optical axis aligned with that of the transmitter, and in which the incoming light is focused on a laser amplifier. The amplifier is supplied with just enough pumping light to bring

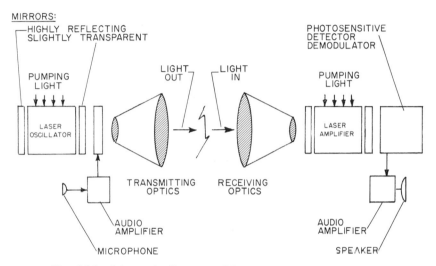

Fig. 14-6 Schematic diagram of laser communication system.

it near the threshold level of stimulated emission, which is thus produced by the signal and amplifies it. This amplified signal goes to a photosensitive detector and demodulator which recovers the audio signals. The laser receiver rejects almost all background noise and is nearly impervious to jamming.

Communications from space platforms to earth and between space ships may be accomplished by lasers, which would require much less power than microwave systems, or systems using incoherent light. This great efficiency is due to the very small divergence of laser beams. A beam from a ruby laser could be concentrated in an area ten-miles wide at a distance of 250,000 miles, equivalent to the distance from the earth to the moon. An ordinary searchlight of like intensity would be spread over an area 25,000 miles wide at that distance. A laser beam directed from the earth to a space station at an altitude of one thousand miles would cover an area only 200 feet in diameter.

On May 9, 1962, a beam of light from a laser was reflected from the moon in an historic test of the capabilities of this device for space communication; that laser was cooled by liquid nitrogen to limit the heating of the ruby crystal at the high power level at which it was operated. Four 2-million watt lamps were used to pump 8000 joules of energy into the crystal in 1/100 of a second. Each 1/2000 second burst of light from the laser carried 50 joules of light energy.

Figure 14-7 shows a possible laser anti-missile system which

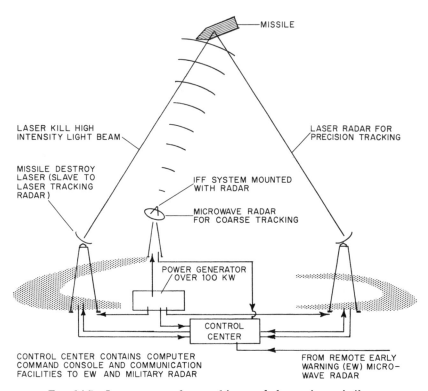

FIG. 14-7   Laser system for tracking and destroying missiles.

uses a microwave radar for coarse tracking. When the tracking radar finds an incoming target, it would align an optical radar (laser) device for precise tracking. The precise optical radar will actuate the laser which is equipped to destroy the missile by burning a hole in it.

IN INFRA-RED DETECTORS

Heat-seeking devices for anti-aircraft missiles can be used to guide them right up the tailpipe of an enemy jet aircraft, and to destroy it. Such infra-red detectors show improved sensitivity and extension of their range to longer wavelengths when they are operated at low temperatures. These benefits are marked at liquid nitrogen temperatures, and are further accentuated by at those of liquid helium. At such low temperatures, the sensitivity and accuracy of the devices are improved so greatly that the guidance mechanism can sense an enemy target at four times the distance previously believed possible.

Infra-red devices have a number of advantages over radar equipment as a method of detection. They are simpler, smaller and cheaper, requiring little auxiliary equipment; they have greater angular accuracy and no minimum range limitations; they can be used at low angles to ground or sea; they do not transmit signals which can betray their positions; and they are difficult to jam. The combination of these many advantages with the increased sensitivity afforded by cryogenic operation yields a powerful device. Its application has been limited chiefly by the extent to which it is subject to interference by fog and other weather conditions.

Infra-red cell cooling systems are of one of three general types. The first is shown in Figure 14-8. It is an open-cycle system that expands the coolant and requires refilling for repeated use. The second is a closed-cycle system incorporating a small gas compressor in series with a heat exchanger and an expander. A third type uses a compressed gas in combination with a compact Joule-Thomson liquefier to furnish cryogenic temperatures upon demand. The open-cycle system is reliable, but has limited opera-

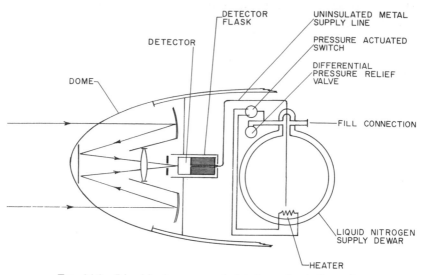

FIG. 14-8   Liquid nitrogen cooled infra-red missile seeker.

tional life. The closed-cycle and compressed gas systems have the advantage of long life at the expense of increased complexity and reduced reliability.

Detectors for the far infra-red (radiation in the range of wavelengths from about 10 to 1000 microns) require cooling to liquid hydrogen and liquid helium temperatures. Such detectors are useful at present for laboratory research purposes and as space research develops they will undoubtedly be required in space vehicles.

Cryogenic cooling increases the sensitivity of infra-red devices for applications in fields other than missiles and space vehicles. A recently developed technique indicates that a 5-minute infra-red examination may pinpoint those transistors in a microcircuit which will be the first to fail several thousand hours later. The same technique may be used to monitor internal circuit operating conditions and to detect discrepancies in design and causes of malfunction within components. This method is rapid, inexpensive and non-destructive. It is based on the simple fact that the operating temperature of a component is a major factor affecting its reliability and life, and that cryogenic infra-red is an ideal way of measuring such temperatures.

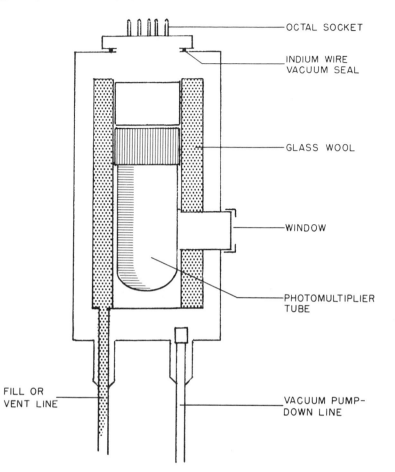

FIG. 14-9   Rocket-borne photo multiplier cryostat.

IN PHOTOMULTIPLIER TUBES

The sensitivity of a photomultiplier tube is greatly increased by operating its cathode at low (liquid nitrogen) temperatures. Since the primary function of photomultiplier tubes is the amplification of incident light, these tubes are used in rocket borne spectrographs to construct a spectrum of the upper atmosphere to assist in determining its composition.

Figure 14-9 shows the cryostat developed to cool such a tube in a rocket-mounted application. Figure 14-10 shows the constancy of signal output, and the greatly decreased background noise as a result of the cryostat mounting. This permits accurate amplification of even a weak light signal without undue interference.

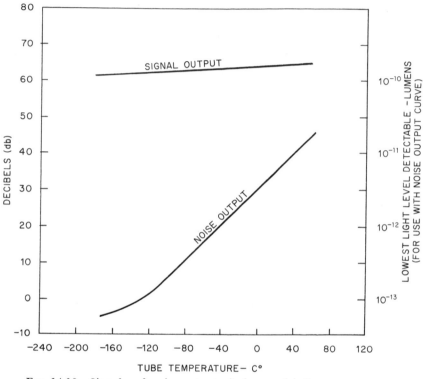

FIG. 14-10   Signal and noise output of photomultiplier vs. temperature.

Chapter 15

HOW COLD IS USED
—IN SUPERCONDUCTIVE DEVICES

Superconductivity is one of the most intriguing phenomena known to physicists and has given rise to much of present-day cryophysics. As discussed in Chapter 6, superconductivity occurs at temperatures close to absolute zero, which vary somewhat for different metals and alloys. There are a number of theories of the phenomenon — that of Fröhlich and Bardeen, which attributes it to interaction between the conduction electrons and the lattice vibrations of the solid, was mentioned in Chapter 6.

The first commercial application of superconductivity was made during World War II in a bolometer for infra-red detection. (A bolometer is a very sensitive thermometric instrument of the metallic resistance type, used for measuring radiant energy.) Rather than operating in the smooth portion of the curve shown in Figure 6-6, the superconductive bolometer operated at the transition temperature where its superconductivity begins. Niobium nitride, was the superconducting material, and helium cooling were used to maintain the niobium nitride strip at its superconducting transition temperature, 15°K. A small amount of incident radiant heat warmed the strip above its transition temperature (the critical point in the conductivity curve) and so effected a large conductivity change. The sensitively of this device, and its speed, made possible rapid detection of enemy troops and equipment.

The magnetic mirror effect produced by superconductors has given rise to a proposal of a frictionless magnetic bearing in which the rotating member would ride on a cushion of magnetic flux. Figure 15-1 shows the design of such a bearing. A superconductive coil is surmounted by a superconductive disc which can move vertically but not laterally. Pushing the disc down compresses the magnetic flux, thus raising the flux density. This increases the current in the coil and amplifies the repellent force of the flux.

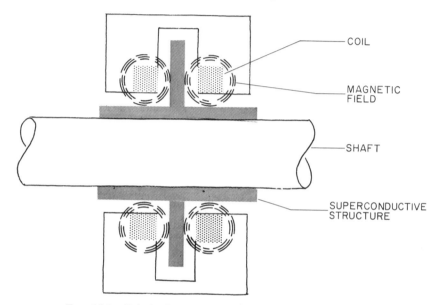

FIG. 15-1   Frictionless superconductive magnetic bearing.

The same magnetic insulating property of superconductors has given rise to a proposal for using superconductive shields to eliminate stray flux lines and shape magnetic fields precisely. In this way the resolving power of electron microscope lenses (See Figure 15-2) could be improved, giving greater resolving power and sharper images.

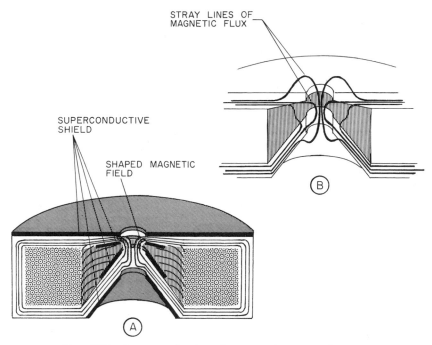

FIG. 15-2   Superconductive electron microscope lenses.

CRYOGENIC MAGNETS

The possibility of operating an electromagnet in a superconductive state in which the current would circulate endlessly and the magnetic field would be perpetually available has long intrigued investigators. It is said that the idea occurred to Onnes shortly after he discovered the phenomenon of superconductivity. In the 1930's, later workers at the University of Leiden pursued the idea further but without success. All of these early experiments encountered a common problem — the magnetic field generated destroyed the superconductivity.

The revolution in cryogenic magnets occurred when workers learned that there were so-called "soft" superconductors (such as aluminum, tin, mercury, and lead) in distinction to a newly-discovered class of "hard" superconductors (which are inter-metallic compounds such as niobium-tin and vanadium-gallium).

The "soft" materials carry the superconductive current only in a thin surface layer and this superconductivity is easily destroyed by magnetic fields. The "hard" materials appear to carry the superconductive current in thin filaments throughout their structure and are relatively quite resistant to the effects of magnetic fields.

The pay-off in superconducting magnets can be illustrated by considering a 50,000 gauss magnet — a magnet which produces 100,000 times the strength of the earth's magnetic field. A conventional electro-magnet capable of producing such a field would have an iron core weighing several tons and a high current coil consisting of a heavy copper bus bar. It would need a 50 kilowatt power supply and provision for removing most of this power as heat. In contrast, a superconducting magnet of equivalent field strength would be ten inches in inside diameter, would weigh one pound (200 pounds including refrigeration) and could be operated by a 6-volt automotive storage battery. Once the cryogenic magnet is at full power, the only power required is that used by the refrigerator which keeps the magnet cold.

PLASMA PHYSICS APPLICATIONS

The practical application of plasma physics to the design and construction of a controlled thermonuclear reactor involves a number of formidable experimental problems.

The first of these is the attainment of the kindling temperature of the thermonuclear reaction, a temperature of perhaps 100 million degrees Kelvin. The second problem is confinement of the hot plasma for finite periods of time; this is done by powerful magnetic fields. In the case of the experimental Model C Stellarator at Princeton University, the magnetic fields are excited by three motor-generator sets, each driven by a 7000-horse power electric motor. The third problem is the operation of the reactor to produce net power, that is, to produce more power than that supplied to the magnets, so that the device can be a practical source of power.

Superconducting magnets, which require only enough power for the refrigeration required to maintain superconductivity, would seem to provide the answer to the second and third of these problems. The new materials mentioned above, which remain superconductive in high-intensity magnetic fields, would meet these requirements. Thus, limitless power in the future, when fossil and even uranium fuels are depleted, may depend for its realization on cryogenics.

SUPERCONDUCTIVE TRANSFORMERS

Revolutionary developments in current transformers are possible by application of superconductivity. If the secondary coil were operated at superconductive temperatures, its current would not be dissipated, and would remain constant indefinitely, or until the transformer input is varied.

Figure 15-3 shows the essentials of a superconductive trans-

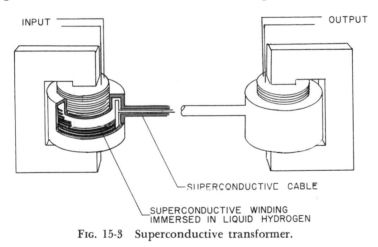

FIG. 15-3   Superconductive transformer.

former. Due to their low specific resistance, the windings of such transformers have no power losses, even when they are greatly reduced in size and weight, with consequent saving of material. The cores of these transformers do not require refrigeration, since only the coils are cooled.

When it is desired to route currents of the order of several hundred amperes into a cryogenic environment, such as a cold test chamber, superconductive transformers are ideal because they provide thermal as well as electrical insulation. However, the most attractive field of application for these transformers will undoubtedly be in the next generation of power generating and transmitting equipment. Figure 15-4 shows a proposed supercon-

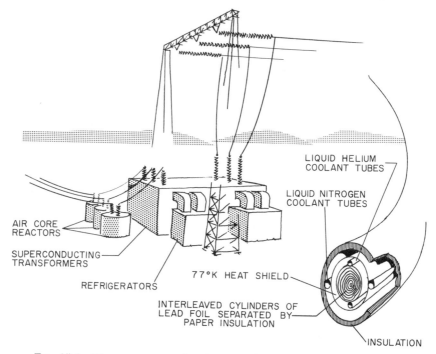

FIG. 15-4   How a superconducting transformer station might look.

ductive transformer station and superconducting transmission line. Such a setup would have much to offer in the way of low electrical losses and small equipment size. Problems involved would be the practical ones of providing cooling of high reliability at low cost. At first sight, the cost of superconductors for commercial distribution of electricity would seem higher than economically feasible. However, even the ordinary underground power lines have an initial cost of $1,000,000 per mile or more. Since one would tend to use high currents in superconductive lines, rather than the high voltages used in conventional transmission lines, the cost of the former for a given power capacity might indeed be lower.

SUPERCONDUCTIVE MOTORS

While ordinary electric motors must be thermally insulated to avoid bearing lubrication problems at very low temperatures, it is now possible to design special motors which are essentially free of internal electrical and mechanical losses. These new motors contain rotors which float in liquid helium, helium gas, or high vacuum, being supported by a cushion of magnetic flux set up by the superconducting stator coils. A schematic drawing of a superconductive motor is shown in Figure 15-5. It is to be noted there that the rotor has a hexagonal shape, in contrast with the cylindrical form used in the conventional motor.

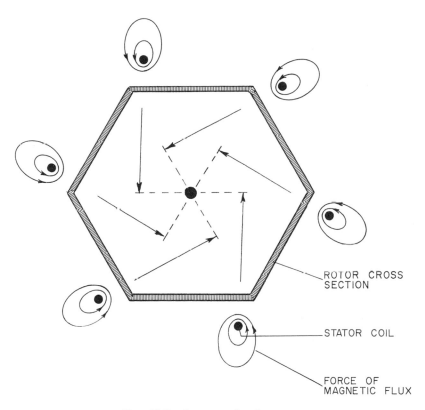

Fɪɢ. 15-5 Superconductive motor.

A problem with truly superconducting motors is that direct shaft output of the power produced is feasible only where the motor is operating another cryogenic device, such as a liquid helium pump. Otherwise the heat-transfer and sealing problems involved in transmitting power to a device operating at higher temperatures, such as those in the atmospheric range, would probably more than offset the advantages of the superconducting motor.

In addition to superconductive motors, there is another class of motors which operates at low, but not superconductive temperatures — the cryogenic motor shown in Figure 15-6. They also have the advantage of small size per unit output, though not as small, of course, as the superconductive motors.

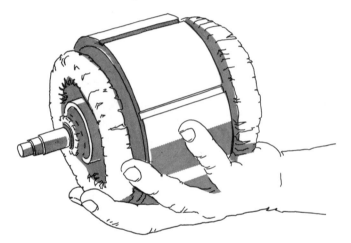

FIG. 15-6   Cryogenic liquid — cooled induction motor.

SUPERCONDUCTIVE GYROSCOPES

Many of the uses of gyroscopes, such as those in navigation and guidance systems, require continued, uniform operation. The friction in their mechanical bearings tends to slow their speed. Therefore, a promising possibility is the elimination of mechanical bearings by suspending a superconducting rotor in a magnetic field. This application should grow in importance with the use of inertial guidance systems for missiles.

SUPERCONDUCTIVE SWITCHES

The cryotron, the first superconductive switch, was announced in 1955 as a result of research by Dudley Buck at the Lincoln Laboratory at M.I.T. In its simplest form the cryotron consists of a fine niobium wire which is wrapped around a tantalum wire. Although both of these metals are potential superconductors, niobium has a greater resistance to magnetic fields in its superconductive state. Thus, with the combination at a temperature near 0°K, it is possible to pass current through the niobium winding and switch the tantalum from being superconductive to being non-superconductive. The voltage passing through the tantalum wire is therefore a function of the current in the niobium control winding. The application of this device is thus closely similar to that of a grid-controlled triode vacuum tube. An important feature is that the current changes in the tantalum wire can then be used to control a second similar device. Such a wire-wound cryotron acts in about 150 microseconds or more, which is relatively slow compared to ferrite core devices which can be switched in about one microsecond.

This deficiency resulted in the development of thin film cryotrons in which the control strip is lead and the gate is tin. Such a strip cryotron uses a thin film of silicon monoxide, deposited from the vapor state, as a base and another such film to separate the metallic elements of the switch (See Figure 15-7). This device

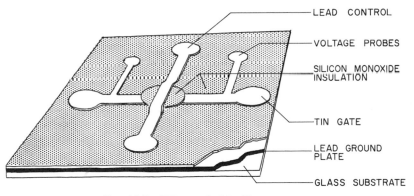

LEAD CONTROL

VOLTAGE PROBES

SILICON MONOXIDE INSULATION

TIN GATE

LEAD GROUND PLATE

GLASS SUBSTRATE

Fig. 15-7 Wire and thin-film cryotrons.

has an operating time of about 1/100 of a microsecond. The lead control strip may be only 6/1000 of an inch wide, the tin gate only $\frac{1}{8}$ inch wide and the lead, tin and silicon monoxide layers only 0.00001 inch thick.

Some 135 such cryotrons can be fabricated into a memory plane the size of a postage stamp, which is formed from about 20 layers of metal and insulating material. Each layer is evaporated onto the glass substrate through a precision-made pattern or mask. The mask for each layer is put into register by an automatic mask changer system which operates inside the vacuum chamber in which the materials are deposited. The control techniques are so sensitive that the evaporation process can form lines finer than a human hair and metallic films so thin that they are invisible to the naked eye.

COMPUTER APPLICATIONS

Tiny superconducting switches offer the intriguing possibility of scaling down the size of a digital computer without reducing its capacity or speed. Dudley Buck predicted that it would be possible to build cryogenic circuits with more than 10^{10} components per cubic inch — a density greater than that of human brain cells! Instead of tubes, transistors, and magnetic cores, the new computers use thousands of bits of metal deposited in microscopic amounts on thin films to achieve switching speeds 50 times those which can be attained by the fastest transistor. In addition to high switching speeds, the cold computer would have a very large memory. Layer upon layer of the thin film elements can be packed into the volume of a bread box. (See Figure 15-8). One such computer is now able to search 300,000 bits of information in its cryogenic memory and pick out the needed data in 50 microseconds.

In a recent conference on very low temperature engineering in Great Britain, it was stated that computer memories totally immersed in a bath of liquid helium can be constructed. Fast computers with very large memories of more than 10^7 bits, would be constructed from memories of this size. Switching times

Fig. 15-8   Computer memories — room temperature at left and cryogenic at right — a size comparison.

of individual elements may be 10 nanoseconds or even less, although the time constants of associated circuits may increase the switching time by a factor of 3 or 4. A 1-5 watt, closed-cycle, helium refrigerator would be used to cool the memory, which would be cubical in shape with edges about one foot long. The cube would contain storage elements packed to a density of over 200 per cubic centimeter. This memory unit should be available commercially by 1965.

A Collins-type helium liquefier to cool a 10^7 bit computer memory has been estimated to cost $50,000. This figure is not very different, it is pointed out, from the cost of an air-conditioning plant to keep a large modern computer of similar storage capacity at a controlled humidity and temperature.

Of course, there are other practical and psychological problems associated with the use of a computer at liquid helium temperatures. The first is refrigeration reliability, which is extremely important because the computer loses its memory irretrievably if it becomes warm. However, the increased dependability of cryogenic hardware and the use of standing equipment have all but eliminated this hazard. Secondly, trouble shooting and parts replacement under liquid helium cause a number of difficulties. Yet improved component designs and remote handling techniques can overcome these difficulties. The development of reliable cold memories for computers will go far to realize the goal of installing computers of the size of the IBM 7090 into rockets and satellites in order to facilitate the transmission of information back to earth, and even to render the space vehicles independent of terrestrial control.

It is to be noted that cryogenic cooling has applications in the computer field not only for cooling memories, but also in the manufacturing operations producing the thin-film components of those memories. Cryogenic pumping is used to produce the high vacuum in which the thin metallic films are deposited.

Chapter 16

HOW COLD IS USED—IN NUCLEAR
AND HIGH ENERGY PHYSICS

The detection of high energy particles from accelerators depends heavily on cryogenics today; the production of such particles may be accomplished in cryogenic devices tomorrow. Of broader interest to industry as well as to science is the study of the effects of nuclear radiation on materials, which can be observed more clearly at low temperatures at which the thermal effects are less pronounced. Higher temperatures are attended by more rapid molecular motion and greater disorder, so that low temperatures permit the observation and measurement of phenomena which would be difficult or impossible to study at ordinary temperatures.

IN BUBBLE CHAMBERS

A most important method of studying atomic structure is by the impact upon target atoms of atomic particles which have been accelerated to speeds approaching that of light. The speed and trajectory of the products of the collisions are analyzed to determine their nature. One of the best ways of making such an analysis is to pass the particles, if they are electrically charged (ions), through a chamber containing liquid hydrogen, which is used because a unit volume of it contains more hydrogen nuclei than an equal volume of paraffin or liquid propane.

The liquid hydrogen is held under pressure at a temperature

that will be above its boiling point, when the pressure is reduced. Just before the particles hit the liquid hydrogen, the pressure is suddenly reduced, so that the liquid hydrogen is superheated. It is therefore ready to form bubbles at any inhomogeneity, so that the charged particles cause tracks of tiny bubbles to form in their wakes. A precisely timed electronic flash permits a picture of the particle tracks to be taken. The presence of a magnetic field from an external electromagnet bends the paths of the charged particles to an extent determined by their speed, mass and charge, so that their nature can be determined from the path. See Figure 16-1 for a cross-sectional view of a typical liquid hydrogen bubble chamber.

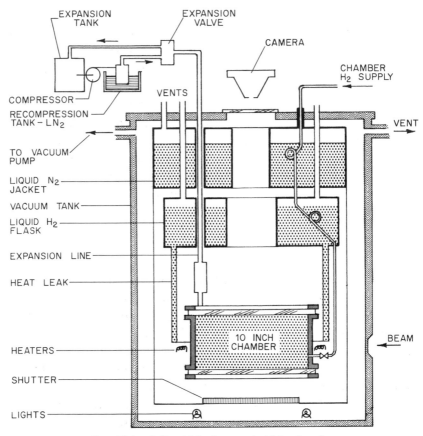

FIG. 16-1 A liquid hydrogen bubble chamber.

Future developments in bubble chamber design will probably include superconducting magnets to provide the required magnetic fields. This seems a natural development since liquid hydrogen will be available anyway.

ACCELERATOR APPLICATIONS

The proton linear accelerator is an attractive device for nuclear research but it is a very complicated machine to build, largely because of the huge amounts of radio-frequency power required (about 60 KW for every Mev gained by the beam). Thus it is necessary to operate such machines in a pulsed manner even though continuous operation would be very desirable if it could be attained.

The application of superconductors to the construction of the radio-frequency cavity could cut down resistive power dissipation in its walls by a factor perhaps as large as 10^4. In this way, a present-day pulsed machine requiring a power of one megawatt might be replaced by one in which the power dissipation was measured only in hundreds of watts. It has been estimated by workers at Harwell in England that costs of construction and operation of a continuously-operated proton accelerator would not be much greater than that of a conventional pulsed accelerator.

IN RADIATION EFFECTS ON MATERIALS

Many advantages are gained by the study of materials at very low temperature — near absolute zero. At such low temperatures, the interfering effects of thermal motion of atoms within the material are greatly reduced and the measurement of atomic and nuclear events can be studied without those complications.

When a block of cobalt-60 is immersed in liquid helium, the cooling has the effect of producing an alignment of the atoms that is essentially undisturbed by thermal motion. This procedure permitted the demonstration of the non-conservation of parity in the beta decay of cobalt-60, based upon the distinction between left-handedness and right-handedness in the spin of products of the weak nuclear reactions.

Early attempts to measure radiation damage in materials were based on observations at or near room temperature. It was soon recognized that some of these effects might be mobile, and that true observations could be made only if the changes were frozen into the material during bombardment and subsequently studied under controlled low-temperature conditions. If the sample is allowed to heat to room temperature before study, the damage may "heal" and give an erroneous indication of radiation effects.

An intense beam of slow neutrons for radiation studies may be obtained by a cryogenic device consisting of a cube of heavy ice (solid deuterium oxide) measuring about a foot on a side, which is located inside an experimental nuclear reactor and cooled to about $20°K$. Fast neutrons passing through the block are slowed and provide the intense beam of slow neutrons. Installations of this type are planned for the Gaithersburg, Maryland reactor of the National Bureau of Standards and the Argonne National Laboratory in Illinois.

Figure 16-2 shows an in-pile loop for the study of the effects of radiation on materials at liquid nitrogen temperatures. This particular device was developed by Jacques Doulat and his co-workers at the Center of Nuclear Studies of the French Atomic Energy Commission at Grenoble in the French Alps. Such devices must be carefully designed and operated to keep oxygen out of the liquid nitrogen, because oxygen concentrates in the cold bath and forms unstable ozone or oxygen-nitrogen compounds under the influence of the nuclear radiation. Indeed, explosions have been common in less sophisticated devices of this type. The pure "primary" nitrogen provides the high-purity bath in which the sample to be studied is immersed. The "secondary" nitrogen is of usual commercial purity, but is used only in a "cold finger" and is kept isolated from the "primary" nitrogen circuit. The lead screens protect the pool of liquid "secondary" nitrogen from nuclear radiation. The loop is composed largely of an aluminum alloy. It has been used quite successfully in experiments in a swimming-pool reactor at Grenoble.

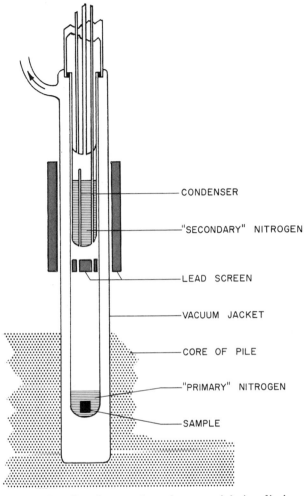

Fig. 16-2   In-pile nitrogen loop for materials irradiation.

IN RADIOACTIVE WASTE DISPOSAL

Radioactive krypton and xenon are among the waste products from nuclear reactors. Conventional methods of removal and disposal of these products are attended by a number of problems. However, one pound of activated charcoal in an absorption bed at cryogenic temperatures removes as much radioactive krypton and xenon from the gas stream of that reactor as one ton of the same charcoal at room temperature. The radioactive elements can then be held in the cold charcoal until it is safe to release them. Such a scheme is used to clean the hydrogen blanketing gas from the reactor in the first United States nuclear merchant ship, the N. S. Savannah.

Chapter 17

HOW COLD IS USED
—IN CHEMICAL PROCESSES

Cryogenics is important to many chemical processes in which low temperatures never enter, the reason being that the production materials used in those industries are obtained by cryogenic processes. The outstanding case is the separation of oxygen and nitrogen from air by cryogenic methods. These elements are then used in many industries as gases at ordinary temperatures. These applications, while not cryogenic per se, are discussed in this chapter.

OXYGEN

The use of oxygen, separated from the air by cryogenic means, in chemical processing is one of the world's big businesses today and one that is still growing apace. There is a ton of oxygen being separated from the air every second somewhere in the world — about half of it going into steelmaking and about half into the manufacture of chemicals, such as ammonia.

The philosophy of providing oxygen is changing as well. Instead of building an oxygen plant just big enough for the oxygen-consuming process and venting the coproduct nitrogen to the atmosphere, the trend is more to consider an air-separation plant as a central power plant. Just as the power plant is built large and flexible enough to meet growing and changing needs for electricity, high pressure and low-pressure steam, so the air separation plant is becoming regarded as a central utility to meet changing and growing demands for oxygen and nitrogen.

In Steel Manufacture

Oxygen is used to perform several important functions in a steel mill. Its major use today is in the conversion of hot pig iron and scrap into steel in an open hearth furnace, an electric furnace, or in special oxygen-fed converters. Its major potential use is found one step earlier in the steel-making process — in oxygen enrichment of the blast in blast furnaces. For finished steel, oxygen has important uses in welding, cutting and scarfing (a flame cutting technique for burning defects from the surfaces of billets and slabs).

As of 1960, open hearth furnaces accounted for 50% of the oxygen consumed by the steel industry, scarfing operations, 25%, blast furnaces, 12% and the other uses, 13%.

The average steel mill today probably uses 500 to 600 cubic feet (50 - 60 pounds) of oxygen in making a ton of steel, primarily in the open hearth furnace. This figure may be increased by a factor of 3 or 4 if oxygen lances are used to a greater extent. However the greatest potential for expansion, as indicated above, is in oxygen enrichment of the air blast in blast furnaces; enrichment of the air to 35% oxygen would require 1000 pounds of oxygen for every ton of pig iron produced.

In the Open Hearth. Over 80% of the steel made in the United States today is produced in open-hearth furnaces. The primary function of the furnace is to reduce the carbon content of the charge by its oxidation to carbon monoxide. This oxidation was traditionally accomplished by adding iron oxide to the molten charge which is heated by flames sweeping back and forth over its surface. As carbon monoxide is produced, it "boils" out of the charge, mixing it so that the iron oxide reaches and reacts with the other impurities, such as silicon and phosphorus, forming their oxides. Limestone is then added and decomposes into calcium oxide (lime) and carbon dioxide. The lime neutralizes the oxides of silicon and phosphorus, limiting their attack upon the furnace lining; while the carbon dioxide reacts with carbon in the charge to give carbon monoxide. The silicon and phosphorus end up as compounds in the slag.

In this process, as conventionally conducted with air as the gas above the molten charge in the furnace, the various reactions in the charge do not furnish all the heat needed, so that additional heat must be supplied by combustion of gaseous or liquid fuel, which limits the capacity of the furnace to that of a charge which can be adequately heated. The use of oxygen makes possible the oxidation of the carbon with a net heat production, which permits operation of open-hearth furnaces at 130% or more of their previous production levels. Oxygen is added today in most plants by using an oxygen lance which burns a mixture of natural gas and oxygen (See Figures 17-1 and 17-2).

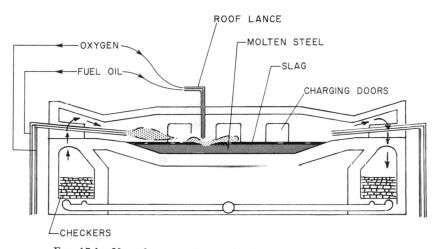

FIG. 17-1 Use of oxygen lances in the open hearth furnace.

In the L-D Converter. This converter was developed in an attempt to combine the high throughput capabilities of a Bessemer converter with the quality attainment of the open-hearth furnace. It is named L-D after the Austrian towns of Linz and Donawitz, the locations of the two steel mills where the process was developed. There are other similar converters in use: one

FIG. 17-2   Oxygen injection in the open hearth furnace.

is the Swedish Kaldo rotating converter and another is the German Rotor, which is a rotating horizontal cylindrical converter.

In an ordinary Bessemer converter, air is blown up through the bottom and it passes through the charge, oxidizing the impurities. In the course of this operation, however, the nitrogen in the air is partially retained in the metal. Substitution of pure oxygen for the air in a conventional Bessemer converter would damage the refractory lining. Hence the L-D concept was developed (See Figure 17-3) in which a water-cooled oxygen lance is inserted into the top of the bottle-shaped converter to burn the impurities out of the steel.

In the Electric Furnace. Electric furnaces account for less than

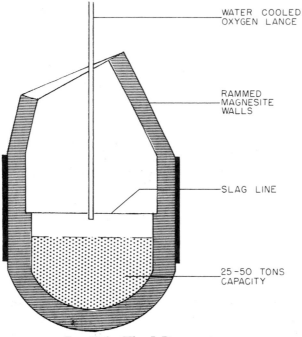

WATER COOLED
OXYGEN LANCE

RAMMED
MAGNESITE
WALLS

SLAG LINE

25-50 TONS
CAPACITY

FIG. 17-3 The L-D converter.

10% of United States steel capacity and are used primarily for making stainless steel. Oxygen can be used in the electric furnace to drive out carbon or to add heat. It is even possible to withdraw the electrodes and supply all the heat by means of oxygen. The installation of an oxygen lance in an electric furnace is shown in Figure 17-4.

In the Blast Furnace. Some oxygen is now used in blast enrichment and plant-scale trials to determine optimum operating techniques are in progress around the world (See Figure 17-5). Oxygen enrichment is employed in making ferromanganese to save fuel and time, but its more general use requires a detailed economic analysis of a particular producing location, to determine whether it is profitable. When additional pig iron production is required, however, the industry will probably turn to oxygen in conjunction with natural gas or fuel oil to boost production without building additional furnaces.

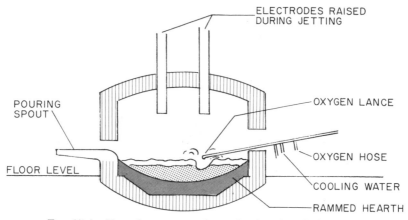

FIG. 17-4   Use of an oxygen lance in the electric furnace.

In Copper Manufacture

The impact of oxygen on future methods of copper manufacture may rival the effect it has had on the steel industry. A
million tons per year of copper are produced in the United States,
and a likely figure for oxygen consumption is 1400 cubic feet
(about 116 pounds) per ton of the metal. Figure 17-6 shows the
points of application of oxygen in the roaster, reverberatory
furnace, and converter of a new pilot plant built by one of the
major United States copper producers.

In Chemical Manufacture

The major uses of oxygen in the chemical industry today are
in the partial oxidation of the hydrocarbons in natural gas and
fuel oil to produce synthesis gas for ammonia and methanol
manufacture, or to produce acetylene. In the latter case, the
useful products obtained are chiefly acetylene and hydrogen,
while in the former case, the products are carbon monoxide and
hydrogen. Both of these are used in making methanol, or the
hydrogen is separated for combination with nitrogen to make
ammonia.

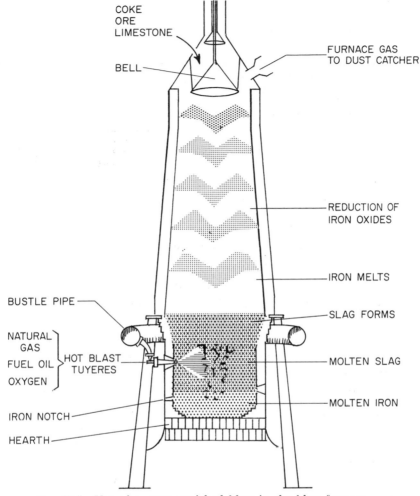

FIG. 17-5   Use of oxygen enriched blast in the blast furnace.

These three products, acetylene, methanol and ammonia account for perhaps 75% of the oxygen used by the chemical industry today. The remainder is consumed in the manufacture of such chemicals as acetaldehyde, ethylene oxide, and hydrogen cyanide.

In the manufacture of hydrogen cyanide, the use of oxygen rather than air in the three-way reaction of natural gas, ammonia and oxygen has a number of advantages which are generally to be found in the use of oxygen in place of air in chemical processing.

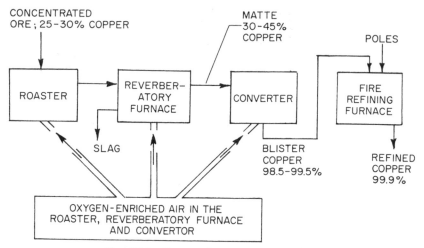

FIG. 17-6   Oxygen in copper processing.

(1). A smaller reactor is required since 4 cubic feet of nitrogen do not accompany every cubic foot of oxygen. (2). Separation of the product is simpler since there is no nitrogen scrubbing operation. (3). Yield is higher due to easier product recovery. (4). There is less danger of air pollution due to simplified removal of the hydrogen cyanide from the reaction products.

Some reactions can be conducted only with oxygen, since the diluent nitrogen in the air would prevent the attainment of the minimum necessary reaction temperature. Such a reaction is the new technique for making raw materials for chemical manufacture from crude oil in a single step (See Figure 17-7) developed by Badische Anilin-und Soda Fabrik at Ludwigshafen/Rhine in Germany.

In the Ceramic Industries

It is possible to increase the capacity of a cement kiln 30% by using oxygen enrichment of the combustion air fed to gas-fired cement kilns. Little or no change in the kiln is required. Firing of glass furnaces with oxygen-enriched air is gaining commercial acceptance in the United States.

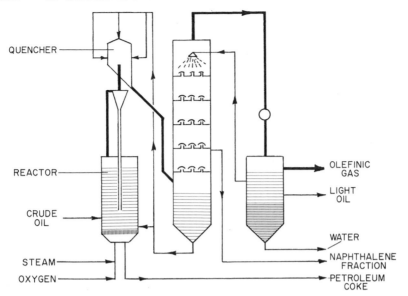

Fig. 17-7 Conversion of crude oil to raw materials for chemicals in a single step using oxygen.

In Waste Disposal

The economic recovery of useful products from wastes and the avoidance of conflict with local pollution regulations has made scientific waste disposal even more important. In the pulp and paper industry, stream pollution problems during the two dry summer months have been solved by one Southern mill by burning wastes with the aid of purchased liquid oxygen. Sulfur values may be recovered simultaneously.

In Explosives

The use of liquid oxygen in explosives is not as important commercially today as in the past. Carl von Linde made the first liquid air explosives in 1897 in Germany. An early use of liquid oxygen explosives, as reported in the French civil engineering journal *Le Genie Civil* in 1899, was in boring the Simplon tunnel through the Alps from Switzerland to Italy. Pulverized charcoal was added to liquid air; to this mixture was added one third of its weight of cotton. A sponge-like substance was obtained which could replace dynamite and which had the advantage of losing its explosive properties in 10 minutes. An early Linde machine was used to produce 7 liters of liquid air per hour for the Simplon tunnel project.

Liquid oxygen explosives (often designated LOX) are mechanical mixtures of liquid oxygen with carbon black. Paper or cloth cartridges containing the carbon black are immersed in liquid oxygen just prior to use. Impregnation time is perhaps one-half hour, and the cartridges must then be used within the next half hour before the oxygen is lost by evaporation. Detonation is effected by electric blasting caps or primer cord. Liquid oxygen explosives have about the same explosive strength as 40% dynamite.

NITROGEN

Nitrogen which is marketed directly is invariably produced by air separation at low temperatures. (Nitrogen which is produced for use in another step in a process is often obtained by non-cryogenic processes). While there are about 4 tons of nitrogen available for every ton of oxygen produced from the air, only about one-half ton or $\frac{1}{8}$ of the available total is recovered today in the United States.

Nitrogen has three important general uses: as a chemical raw material, as an inert blanketing medium, and as a cryogenic fluid.

For Ammonia

When the ammonia synthesis gas is made by the partial oxidation route, it is natural to build an air separation plant to provide both the oxygen for synthesis gas manufacture and the nitrogen for ammonia manufacture (See Figure 17-8). Even when steam reforming of natural gas is carried out to produce the synthesis gas, or when by-product hydrogen is available from refinery operations or electrolytic chlorine cells, the nitrogen may be produced by air separation.

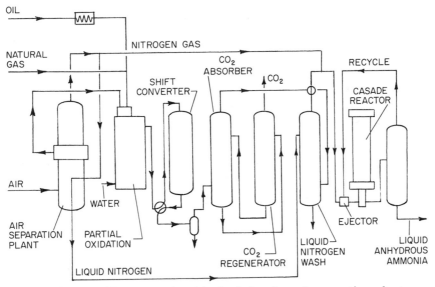

FIG. 17-8   Making ammonia with the help of an air separation plant.

In addition to use of nitrogen as a basic raw material in the synthesis step proper, cryogenic nitrogen may be used to purify the hydrogen in a nitrogen wash process, as shown in Figure 17-8.

For Blanketing Reactive Materials

The use of inert gas generators which remove the oxygen from the air by reaction with a hydrocarbon has long been common practice in the chemical industry. They produce a gas containing perhaps 87% nitrogen, with moisture and hydrocarbons as the main impurities.

However, as more reactive chemicals are produced and handled commercially, and as purity requirements rise in an increasingly sophisticated chemical industry, the demand for a really pure and really inert blanketing gas increases. This demand is being met by high-purity nitrogen from air-separation plants, as the requirements of the chemical industry bring about the construction of such plants to supply oxygen.

In polypropylene manufacture, for example, traces of moisture could be very harmful and high purity nitrogen is essential to provide an inert reaction atmosphere. About 200 cubic feet (15 pounds) of nitrogen are required per ton of polypropylene produced.

In the manufacture of fine chemicals, and particularly of drugs, purity of the blanketing gas is critical. It must not only be inert but clean, both chemically and biologically.

Some applications, such as the blanketing of gasoline in storage to reduce gum formation, are less demanding as regards purity of the blanketing gas. In such cases combustion-type inert gas generators furnish a product of adequate purity. However, the continued increase in the number of air separation plants in oil refinery areas to produce oxygen for petrochemical manufacture can provide a supply of nitrogen which is produced with the oxygen, and which is thus available at economic price levels.

Calcium carbide is one example of a bulk industrial chemical shipped under nitrogen to keep out moisture, which would react with the carbide, depleting its acetylene-producing capacity and creating a hazard during shipment.

The blanketing of hydraulic fluid systems in aircraft is another application of nitrogen to the blanketing of reactive materials.

In Semiconductor Manufacture

In the manufacture of germanium transistors, nitrogen is used both as an inert blanketing medium, and as an inert carrier for doping — that is for carrying controlled amounts of added impurities into the germanium. Note that nitrogen cannot be used in the manufacture of silicon transistors because their processing temperatures are so high that the nitrogen reacts.

Liquid nitrogen cold traps are also used to eliminate moisture and other gaseous impurities from manufacturing operations in semiconductor preparation. In the alloying of aluminum and silicon for semiconductor diodes and transistors, for example, the slightest trace of oxygen, carbon dioxide, or water vapor could ruin the electrical properties of the finished component. The growth of single silicon crystals is another operation in which trace amounts of oxygen or carbon dioxide alter the electrical properties of the crystal, and they must be removed by cold-trapping.

In Metals Refining

Nitrogen can be used as a stripping agent in the deoxidation of metals, as in the refining of aluminum. It is not used in the treatment of iron because of its solubility in the molten metal.

FROZEN FREE RADICALS

The molecular fragments or transient species which exist only momentarily in hot gases found in flames or during rapid chemical reactions are difficult to study. The information obtainable by spectroscropic techniques is limited by the short lives (or half-lives) of the radicals. Now, however, by operating a collector surface at cryogenic temperatures, it is possible to freeze these free radicals in their unstable state and study them at more leisure. Such studies can give invaluable information on the mechanism of chemical reactions, and on their kinetics and energetics.

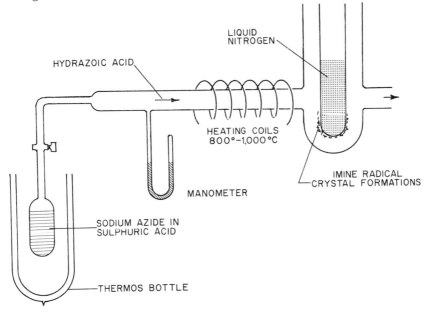

FIG. 17-9 Apparatus for producing and trapping frozen free radicals.

Figure 17-9 shows an apparatus for the production and trapping of free radicals. The flask in the thermos bottle contains a solution of sodium azide in sulfuric acid. This generates hydroazoic acid, HN_3, which is vaporized and which passes through the heating coils of an electric furnace where the vapors are heated to 1000°C. The HN_3 decomposes into nitrogen, N_2, and the imine radical, —HN—. The imine radicals are then condensed on a surface cooled by liquid nitrogen, where they appear as a blue solid. This experiment was performed by Professor F. O. Rice at Catholic University of America in Washington, D. C. Rice, an expert on free radicals, was attempting to duplicate conditions on the planet Jupiter. Jupiter's varicolored markings may well be due to free radicals, frozen solid in the cold (—171°C or —276°F) Jovian atmosphere.

GAMMA RAY CATALYZED REACTIONS

Radiation-induced reactions are often conducted at cryogenic temperatures because reactive intermediates formed by the action of primary radiations and secondary electrons on irradiated media are quite unstable at higher temperatures. The use of low temperatures is possible because the activation of radiation-induced reactions does not decrease with temperature as do most other chemical reactions. On the other hand, temperatures do influence the rate of reaction of intermediates, however formed, with other reactants. Thus, radiation-induced reactions can produce activated intermediates at low temperatures, which can then be made to undergo second-stage reactions to produce products substantially different from those obtained from the same reactants at higher temperatures. Processes of this kind have been patented for petroleum cracking and reforming at liquid nitrogen temperatures under the influence of radiation.

It may be possible to obtain ordered polymers by radiation-catalyzed polymerization at such low temperatures that thermal effects do not hinder orientation of monomer molecules into regularly-ordered chains.

Chapter 18

HOW COLD IS USED
—IN METALS FABRICATION

The last chapter explained how metals are produced and refined to an increasing extent by processes using oxygen separated from air by cryogenic means. In this chapter the actual application of cryogenic temperatures to the processing of metal shapes is considered.

PRECIPITATION HARDENING OF STEEL

Tougher, more ductile steels with improved life characteristics are produced by sub-zero chilling of steel. Depending on the composition of the steel, the Rockwell "C" hardness may also be increased several points through cold treatment. Above 204°C (400°F) as shown in Figure 18-1, steel has a completely austenitic structure. As steel cools, the relatively unstable austenite changes slowly to martensite, which is tougher and more ductile. It is advantageous to accelerate the change because martensite has more desirable properties, and also because warping and distortion occur during the transformation so that a dimensionally accurate part should be made of steel already transformed to martensite.

As shown in Figure 18-1, the austenite content can be reduced from 10% to 3% or less by cooling with liquid nitrogen to —90°C (—130°F).

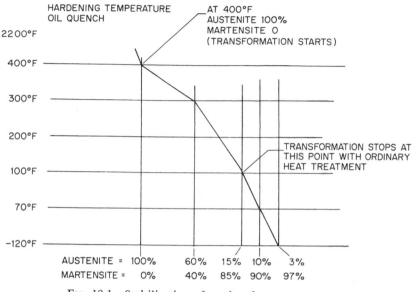

FIG. 18-1   Stabilization of steel at low temperatures.

Hacksaw blades treated at this temperature gave 113% longer life. High speed drills can drill 250 holes after cold treatment as contrasted with 5 to 20 holes without it.

COLD STRETCHING

A variety of low-temperature steel working which is carried out on a welded and fabricated vessel is called Ardeforming. The process is named after the developer, Arde-Portland, Inc. of Paramus, New Jersey. It is claimed that cold treatment after welding produces a much better finished part because it restores the improvement in strength given by prior cold treatment, which was lost during welding.

In the Ardeforming process, the vessel is completely fabricated and any openings are sealed off after fabrication, leaving only a single gas connection. The vessel is then lowered into a bath of liquid nitrogen in an insulated pit where it is cooled to —320°F (—196°C). Then gaseous nitrogen under pressure is introduced into the vessel and held there until the container stretches about 15%, expanding into a stainless steel die of the desired final shape, as shown in Figure 18-2. The vessel is then allowed to

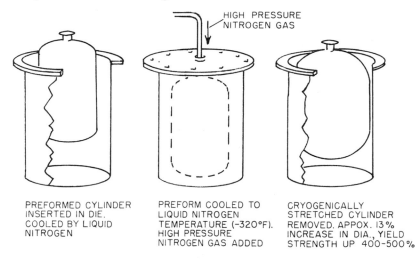

PREFORMED CYLINDER
INSERTED IN DIE.
COOLED BY LIQUID
NITROGEN

PREFORM COOLED TO
LIQUID NITROGEN
TEMPERATURE (-320°F).
HIGH PRESSURE
NITROGEN GAS ADDED

CRYOGENICALLY
STRETCHED CYLINDER
REMOVED. APPOX. 13%
INCREASE IN DIA., YIELD
STRENGTH UP 400-500%

FIG. 18-2   How cold stretching is done.

warm to room temperature. Tensile strength has been improved by a factor of three.

The major application of cold stretching has been in the development of casings for solid-propellent rockets. High strength-weight ratio is achieved, giving a low cost steel vessel competitive in performance with filament-wound glass fiber casings. Other possible uses for products of this process are torpedo cases, as well as high pressure storage spheres and cylinders for gases and liquids. Low-temperature stretching by the Arde-Portland process is simpler, faster, and less expensive than heat treating.

CRYOFORMING

The cryoforming process is a development of Boeing Airplane Company. It is used in the processing of hardenable stainless steel sheets. The machined, formed, or welded parts made of such steels contain residual stresses which have a tendency to warp the parts, and to cause them to deviate from the desired final dimensions.

The dewarping operation starts with an initial annealing step at 1725°F (941°C). This heating usually causes further temporary distortion, but the part is then cooled to 200°F (93°C) when it is forced into a die which is the exact shape of the finished part. The part and die are then cooled gradually to —100 to —110°F (—73 to —79°C) in a solution of Dry Ice and trichloroethylene or in a dry cold box.

When the part is removed from the cryoforming die, it no longer has a tendency to warp. In addition to fitting design dimensions closely, it can now be age hardened without being restrained to keep it from warping. This process permits manufacture of curved corrugations with multiple radii to close design tolerances.

ZEROLLING

According to experimental data first published about 1950, working stainless steels at subzero temperatures results in a greatly increased tensile strength. If these "zerolled" stainless steels are heated to temperatures up to 800°F (427°C), additional strengthening takes place. This effect is particularly noticeable in type 347 stainless steel.

Although austenitic stainless steels held at —320°F (—196°C) for 100 hours undergo no changes in mechanical properties at room temperature, the mechanical working of such steels at such low temperatures induces a much greater rate of work hardening, with a corresponding increase in tensile strength, yield strength and hardness, compared to steels processed at room temperature. For a given tensile strength, the zerolled sample is more ductile. Furthermore, the desired tensile strength is achieved by much smaller reduction in area through rolling than is the case in room temperature processing.

EXPLOSIVE HARDENING AT LOW TEMPERATURES

Much attention has been given lately to the explosive forming of metals, done with the metal sample at ordinary temperatures. A project conducted at Stanford Research Institute under the sponsorship of the International Nickel Company has investigated another aspect of the explosive treatment of metals. Instead of stretching and deforming warm metals under explosive force, this project had as its object the hardening of metals which were confined so they could not expand or deform. The explosions were conducted at liquid nitrogen temperatures using thick stainless steel sheets. Cryogenic blasting gave improved hardness and better penetration of hardness improvement into the interior of the sheet. This technique offers the possibility of making stronger pressure vessels by using cold-rolled sheets and then hardening the heated and welded areas by explosive shock waves at subzero temperatures.

ALUMINUM STRESS-RELIEVING

Aluminum alloys can be normalized, or stress-relieved, by exposure to temperatures of the order of —130°F (—90°C). The treatment may take 2 3 hours. Using liquid nitrogen at —320°F (—196°C) the time can be reduced to a few minutes and the degree of stress relief increased greatly.

The improvement in physical properties is evident from performance of aircraft parts. In parts where trouble had previously been encountered with seizure or operating failures, dependability was greatly increased by cold treatment. Whereas machining operations performed in rapid sequence has given trouble with ordinary aluminum parts, pre-chilled parts can be rough-machined and immediately finish-machined.

Aging at room temperature for a period of perhaps four days makes aluminum stronger but less workable. Cold treatment delays natural age hardening and can speed subsequent production processes. For example, aluminum rivets are stored at low temperatures to assure improved heading during the riveting operation.

NITROGEN FOR BRIGHT ANNEALING

The bright annealing of stainless steel consumes about 2000 tons per day of nitrogen, a quantity that in 1962 was second only to ammonia manufacture in the consumption of nitrogen produced by air separation. In bright annealing, nitrogen may be used alone or it may be used as a carrier for deoxidizing agents. A typical mixture contains 93% nitrogen and 7% hydrogen.

Bright annealing is also used by steel mills for tin plate, and by the electronics industry in the manufacture of electron tubes and the preparation of glass-to-metal seals. Figure 18-3 shows a

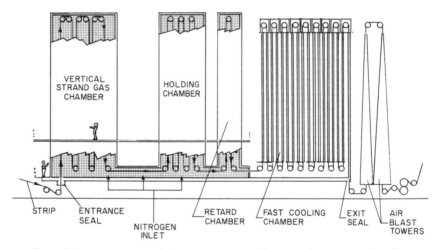

FIG. 18-3   Furnace used for bright annealing continuous steel strip.

furnace used for the continuous bright annealing of steel strip. This model is a so-called tower-type furnace which can handle steel from .007 inch to .015 inch in thickness in widths from 18 to 36 inches at a speed of 1000 feet per minute. Long, low roller-hearth furnaces may also be used to process steel strip continuously or to convey fabricated articles, such as stampings or castings, continuously through the nitrogen-rich atmosphere.

LOW-TEMPERATURE MACHINING

Super alloy steels are finding increasing use in the aircraft and missile industries. Machining such alloys generates terrific heat (up to 2000°F) at the interface between the work and the tool. Galling, local work hardening, and oxidation occur under such conditions, making accurate and precise machining impossible and lowering tool life to uneconomic levels.

The use of carbon dioxide mist cooling at —109°F (—78°C) or the use of Dry Ice to cool solvent which is then used to flood the work at —76°F (—60°C) are two techniques which have been explored by the United States Air Force and Air Force contractors. Improvement of 300% in tool life in machining super alloys has been obtained by application of the mist cooling technique.

It would seem that the combination of low temperature and inert atmosphere which could be provided at low cost by liquid nitrogen would be applicable to an improved method of turning and drilling these super alloys.

Chapter 19

HOW COLD IS USED
— IN MISCELLANEOUS APPLICATIONS

As has been shown in the last ten chapters, the applications of cold are extended into many industries. It is logical to expect that there would be a considerable number of applications which cannot be discussed with reference to a single industry. These miscellaneous applications are the subject of this chapter and serve, it is to be hoped, to provide a fitting conclusion to this book. They illustrate the versatility of the many uses of cold, which promises many more new and exciting uses tomorrow and in the days to come.

POWDERING CHEMICAL PRODUCTS

The embrittlement of materials at low temperatures has been put to good use in the case of plastics. Plastics cooled to liquid nitrogen temperatures can have rough edges removed by a tumbling operation, as in the case of silicone rubber O-rings. More vigorous mechanical treatment, in hammer mills or grinders, can be used to powder plastic materials which are hard to prepare in powder form and which cannot be comminuted at ordinary temperatures since they are thermoplastic and the heat of grinding would soften or melt them.

Figure 19-1 shows a scheme for pulverizing chemicals at low

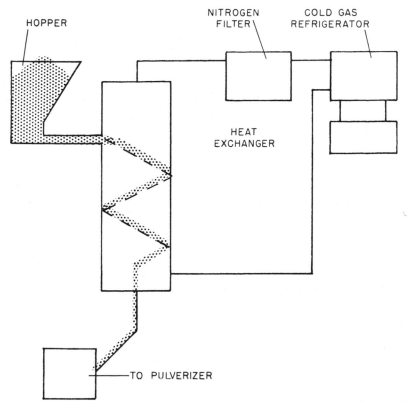

FIG. 19-1 Scheme for pulverizing chemicals at low temperatures using liquid nitrogen.

temperatures using liquid nitrogen. A nitrogen mist is passed upward in an exchanger column countercurrent to the chemical to be processed. The material is then pulverized in the frozen state.

In addition to thermoplastics, such other materials as dyestuffs, spices, insecticides and pharmaceuticals may advantageously be handled in this manner. More rapid pulverization, a greater degree of particle size control, less product damage and increased safety in the pulverizing operation result from the use of this low-temperature technique.

FREEZING PIPELINES FOR REPAIRS

Discontinuance of pipeline flow without valves in order to permit local repairs or the local installation of valves or meters, without the necessity of depressurizing and draining an entire distribution system can be accomplished neatly and economically by a cryogenic method. Boulder, Colorado was faced with the problem of installing water meters in each residence throughout the city. Since valves in the water mains were few and far between, their use for the installation would have required the interruption of service in large areas for long periods of time. By excavating only enough to expose the inlet waterpipe in front of each residence and using a liquid nitrogen freeze box as shown in Figure 19-2, it was possible to install meters at one house at a time with no interruption of service to others. About 1½ quarts

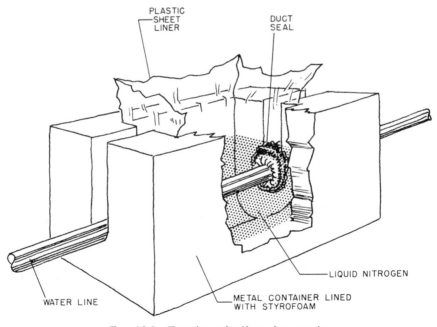

FIG. 19-2 Freezing pipelines for repairs.

of liquid nitrogen froze the line in about one minute, the freeze lasting for 20 minutes, which was enough time to cut and thread the line in the house and install a valve before the new meter. The estimated cost of the nitrogen used was less than one dollar per house.

SHRINK FITTING

Shrink fitting is a process for fitting a slightly oversize inner part into a mating hole by chilling the part to cryogenic temperatures and thus decreasing its diameter. Competitive methods include press fitting or heating the outer part to expand it.

The advantages of cryogenic shrink fitting are simplicity, low investment in equipment, tighter fit because of greater shrinkage, reduction in the scrap loss of press fitting, and reduced labor. Shrink fitting also avoids the danger of softening heat-treated parts, which is possible if heating is used to expand the outer member of the assembly.

A typical application involves the shrink fitting of the splined end of a steel automobile drive shaft into a steel ring gear. The placing of steel bearing inserts into aluminum automobile engine blocks is another application which is attractive because of the poor press-fitting properties of aluminum.

FIGHTING FIRES

One interesting application of liquid nitrogen is in fire fighting, trials of which have been made in forest and brush fires in California. Forest fire fighting has long been a difficult and tedious job. It may require armies of men working furiously in efforts to build fire breaks to contain the fire so that it can burn itself out. More recently huge bulldozers have been used for this purpose where the terrain permits. Still more recently, airborne attack upon forest fires by use of hydrated boron salts as flame retardant agents has been fairly successful.

Tests conducted over the last several years have indicated that liquid nitrogen may be highly effective in combatting these difficult-to-fight fires. Application by special hose truck, by plastic containers used as hand grenades, and by large plastic containers used as aerial bombs have all been considered. Trials indicate that nitrogen is effective in both putting out the fire and in extinguishing afterglow, probably due to a combination of effects, such as the cooling effect of the low-temperature liquid nitrogen, the heat absorbed by its evaporation, and the smothering effect of the nitrogen gas produced. Comparative tests with water and carbon dioxide indicate the superiority of nitrogen. The absence of property damage from nitrogen use led one observer to suggest the possible application of liquid nitrogen to urban fire fighting.

PHOTOGRAPHING INDIVIDUAL METAL ATOMS

The field ion emission microscope is a cryogenic device capable of direct magnifications of 2 million diameters, five to ten times greater than that of present-day electron microscopes, and adequate to reveal individual metal atoms.

The specimen to be studied must be drawn into a needle so fine that it can barely be seen with the naked eye. The needle is mounted as shown in Figure 19-3 and charged to a large positive electric potential at which electron absorption can occur. In this way electrons are drawn into the metal, exposing parts of the sample which project through the electron cloud at the tip. Then helium atoms are pumped past the cold specimen, by filling the chamber with helium after an initial evacuation. Helium is used because it has a very high ionization potential so that any impurities are readily ionized and carried away, producing at worst a faint glow on the screen. The tip may be cooled by liquid nitrogen as shown in Figure 19-3 or, even better, by liquid hydrogen. Hydrogen gives twice the image brightness and somewhat better image definition. As the helium atoms hit the tip they can become ionized and are accelerated by the magnetic field

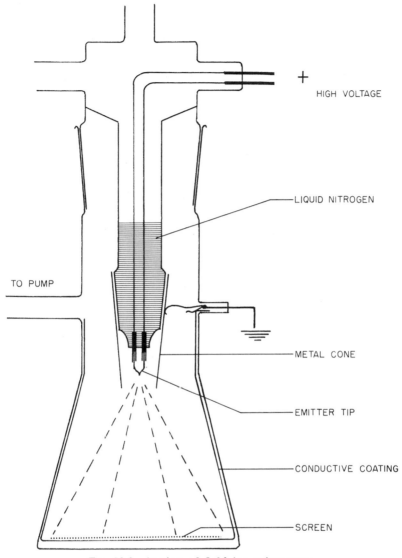

FIG. 19-3   Section of field ion microscope.

to the fluorescent screen, where they produce flashes indicating the location of the atoms with which they collided on the metal surface.

AND SO ON . . .

Cryogenic applications are springing up everywhere. As this book goes to press, new uses include:

— the use of liquid nitrogen to freeze the ground around excavations. Where wet and soggy conditions make it difficult to stabilize the earth wall of an excavation long enough to build forms and pour concrete, freezing the earth with brine has been used. Now liquid nitrogen finds application here.
— the storage of reactive adhesive materials for indefinite periods of time. Epoxy cements are given infinitely long shelf life by storage at liquid nitrogen temperatures. This aids manufacturing control as well as uniformity of field application.

Here again we have cold serving man in a multitude of everyday uses — providing a new dimension for our expanding technology — down to the cold frontier.

INDEX